THE FLASH CHRONICLES

VOLUME TWO

**ALL COVERS AND ART PENCILLED BY CARMINE INFANTINO
AND INKED BY JOE GIELLA, UNLESS OTHERWISE NOTED.**

Julius Schwartz – EDITOR-ORIGINAL SERIES ☆ Bob Harras – GROUP EDITOR-COLLECTED EDITIONS
Bob Joy – EDITOR ☆ Robbin Brosterman – DESIGN DIRECTOR-BOOKS

DC COMICS

Diane Nelson - PRESIDENT ☆ Dan DiDio and Jim Lee - CO-PUBLISHERS
Geoff Johns - CHIEF CREATIVE OFFICER ☆ Patrick Caldon - EVP-FINANCE AND ADMINISTRATION
John Rood - EVP-SALES, MARKETING AND BUSINESS DEVELOPMENT ☆ Amy Genkins - SVP-BUSINESS AND LEGAL AFFAIRS
Steve Rotterdam - SVP-SALES AND MARKETING ☆ John Cunningham - VP-MARKETING ☆ Terri Cunningham - VP-MANAGING EDITOR
Allison Gill - VP-MANUFACTURING ☆ David Hyde - VP-PUBLICITY ☆ Sue Pohja - VP-BOOK TRADE SALES
Alysse Soll - VP-ADVERTISING AND CUSTOM PUBLISHING ☆ Bob Wayne - VP-SALES ☆ Mark Chiarello - ART DIRECTOR

DC Comics, 1700 Broadway, New York, NY 10019
A Warner Bros. Entertainment Company
First Printing.

ISBN: 978-1-4012-2884-2
Printed by Quad/Graphics, Dubuque, IA, USA. 9/01/10

Cover art by Carmine Infantino and Joe Giella

THE FLASH

RETURN OF THE Super-GORILLA!

GRODD, THE AMAZING APE WITH THE MIND OF A GENIUS-- AN EVIL GENIUS-- MAKES A SURPRISE REAPPEARANCE TO CHALLENGE HIS NEMESIS, THE *FLASH*! AND ONCE AGAIN THE *FASTEST MAN ALIVE* COUNTS ON HIS SUPER-SPEED TO OVERWHELM HIS FOE--BUT THIS TIME THE *FLASH'S* SPEED TURNS OUT TO BE THE VERY MEANS BY WHICH *GRODD* PLANS TO DEFEAT THE *SCARLET SPEEDSTER*!

FLASH'S SUPER-SPEED IS CAUSING THE *MOLA*-- THIS UNDERGROUND WORLD'S STRANGE ATMOSPHERE--TO ADHERE TO HIS BODY... AND INSTANTLY SOLIDIFY ON HIM!

ONE MORE STEP AND I'LL STOP *GRODD*... UHH...CAN'T MAKE IT...

AND AS THE RANGER MAKES HIS REPORT...

...AND THEN, WITHIN A MINUTE, THE WATER IN EVERY NEARBY WELL, BROOK, POND, LAKE-- DRIED UP! IT MUST HAVE SOMETHING TO DO WITH THAT BORER!

IN NEWSPAPERS ALL OVER THE COUNTRY BY NOON...

GLOBE NEWS
5¢
STRANGE METALLIC OBJECTS SHOOT UP FROM EARTH!
GOVERNMENT INVESTIGATING UNDERGROUND THREAT!

AND WHILE THE THOUGHTS OF THE NATION ARE FOCUSED ON THE AMAZING MYSTERY, ELSEWHERE-- IN A CITY KNOWN ONLY TO *ONE* MAN IN THE ENTIRE WORLD-- ANOTHER PROBLEM HAS ARRESTED ATTENTION...

IN *GORILLA-CITY*, IN THE HEART OF *SAVAGE AFRICA*, HEAD SCIENTIST *SOLOVAR* FACES AN EMERGENCY...

--AND *GRODD*, OUR MOST DANGEROUS GORILLA, HAS ESCAPED?

YES, *SOLOVAR*...

WE FOUND *GRODD'S* SPECIAL GUARD UNCONSCIOUS-- THE CELL DOOR RIPPED APART! ANALYSIS SHOWS HE COULD HAVE ESCAPED AS LONG AS A *WEEK AGO!* BUT WE ONLY JUST DISCOVERED IT!

THIS IS TERRIBLE NEWS! I PROMISED OUR FRIEND *FLASH* THAT WE WOULD KEEP *GRODD* WELL GUARDED--* NOW WE MUST NOTIFY *FLASH* AT ONCE!

3

* *EDITOR'S NOTE:* IN THE PREVIOUS ISSUE OF THE *FLASH,* THE *FASTEST MAN ALIVE* CAPTURED THE VILLAINOUS *GRODD* AND TURNED HIM OVER TO *SOLOVAR* FOR SAFEKEEPING!

SWIFTLY **SOLOVAR** REACHES FOR AN INSTRUMENT ON HIS DESK...

INFORMATION? GET ME **FLASH'S** VIBRATION-AURA NUMBER! IT MUST BE ON FILE!

FLASH WAS IN **GORILLA-CITY** NOT LONG AGO--AND THE **VIBRATION RECORDERS** WOULD AUTOMATICALLY HAVE REGISTERED HIS VIBRATION-FREQUENCY!

I'LL CHECK, SIR...

SOON...

YOU WERE RIGHT, SCIENTIST **SOLOVAR**! OUR RECORDERS DID REGISTER **FLASH'S** VIBRATION-AURA! THE NUMBER IS **GAMMA FREQUENCY S4-8321!**

CONTACT **FLASH** AT ONCE! I'LL HOLD ON--

YES, SIR!

FROM THE HIDDEN GORILLA-CITY AN ENERGY-BURST FLARES UPWARD...

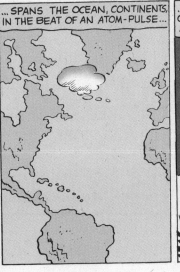

...SPANS THE OCEAN, CONTINENTS, IN THE BEAT OF AN ATOM-PULSE...

...INTO THE POLICE LABORATORY IN CENTRAL CITY WHERE **CHEMIST BARRY ALLEN** WORKS...

HUH? SOMEONE CALLING ME?

As THE YOUNG SCIENTIST STANDS TRANSFIXED...

FLASH! CONTACTING FLASH! THIS IS AN EMERGENCY--!

GREAT SCOTT! I HEAR SOMETHING BUT--

NO ONE IN THE WORLD KNOWS THAT MY SECRET IDENTITY IS THE FLASH! WHO COULD--?

THIS IS SOLOVAR! LISTEN--!

GRODD HAS ESCAPED! YOU MUST GET HERE AS FAST AS POSSIBLE! OUR GORILLA-CITY-- PERHAPS THE EARTH ITSELF-- IS IN DIRE DANGER!

I'M ON MY WAY, SOLOVAR--

GOOD! I'LL BE WATCHING FOR YOU!

A MOMENT LATER IN A SHIELDED CUBICLE, BARRY ALLEN PRESSES A RING ON HIS FINGER...

OUT OF A TINY COMPARTMENT IN THE RING, A MINIATURE FLASH UNIFORM SPRINGS, THAT SWELLS SWIFTLY IN CONTACT WITH AIR...

AND SCARCELY INSTANTS AFTER, A BLUR CROSSES CENTRAL CITY...

I WONDER--COULD THE ESCAPE OF GRODD HAVE ANYTHING TO DO WITH THE APPEARANCE OF THOSE STRANGE METALLIC OBJECTS?

5

THE SCARLET SPEEDSTER'S VIBRATIONS PROPEL HIM ACROSS THE ATLANTIC OCEAN AT A FRACTION OF THE SPEED OF THE FASTEST ROCKET...

WHATEVER HE'S UP TO, GRODD--THE EVIL SUPER-GORILLA--MUST BE FOUND AND RECAPTURED!

THEN, IN AN ISOLATED PART OF AFRICA...

LAST TIME SOLOVAR TOOK ME TO GORILLA-CITY IT WAS SITUATED RIGHT HERE! BUT I CAN'T FIND ANY TRACE OF IT NOW...

SUDDENLY, A CONTACT BY SOLOVAR...

YOU'RE IN THE MIDST OF GORILLA-CITY AT THIS VERY MOMENT, FLASH-- ONLY YOU'RE NOT AWARE OF IT!

WE HAVE A PROTECTIVE MACHINE THAT CUTS OFF OUR CITY FROM THE HUMAN SENSES, THUS PREVENTING ANYONE FROM KNOWING OF ITS EXISTENCE! STAND BY--WE'RE FOCUSING THE MACHINE ON YOU TO BRING YOU INTO OUR FIELD OF VIBRATION!

IN THE BLINK OF AN EYE, THE JUNGLE TERRAIN IS "WIPED OUT OF EXISTENCE" AND REPLACED BY...

GORILLA-CITY!

6

As the **HUMAN COMET** whizzes toward **SOLOVAR'S** laboratory...

A CLEVER TRICK! AND IT EXPLAINS WHY NO AIRCRAFT OR EXPLORER HAS EVER REPORTED SEEING THIS HIDDEN CITY!

THEN, IN THE LABORATORY OF THE CHIEF SCIENTIST OF THE GORILLAS...

GRODD IS POTENTIALLY THE MOST DANGEROUS CREATURE ON EARTH, **SOLOVAR**! HOW DID HE ESCAPE?

HE OUTWITTED US, **FLASH**...

BEFORE YOU LEFT US LAST TIME I TOLD YOU **GRODD** HAD LOST HIS **FORCE OF MIND** POWER THAT MADE HIM SO DANGEROUS! BUT I WAS WRONG! HE ONLY **PRETENDED** TO LOSE IT-- AND HE USED HIS MENTAL POWERS TO EFFECT HIS ESCAPE!

BUT **WHERE** DID HE GO, **SOLOVAR**?

WE'VE BEEN TRYING TO TRACK HIM-- BUT SO FAR **WITHOUT SUCCESS**! HE SEEMS TO HAVE **VANISHED** OFF THE FACE OF THE EARTH!

AT THAT MOMENT MILES BELOW THE EARTH'S CRUST...

WE ARE READY TO FOLLOW YOUR ORDERS, **GRODD**!

GOOD!

THESE BIRD-PEOPLE DON'T REALIZE IT-- BUT SINCE I CAME DOWN HERE A WEEK AGO, THEY'VE ALL FALLEN UNDER THE SPELL OF MY **FORCE OF MIND** POWER!

7

"THE BIRD-PEOPLE LIVE ON FLOATING ISLANDS INSIDE THE EARTH -- WHICH IS *HOLLOW* EXCEPT FOR THE CRUST! THEY NEVER IMAGINED UNTIL *I* TOLD THEM THAT THERE MIGHT BE LIFE *OUTSIDE* THEIR WORLD... "

ONE OF OUR SCIENTISTS THEORIZED LIFE EXISTED ON THE OTHER SIDE OF OUR SKY -- BUT HE WAS LAUGHED AT!

I'VE CONVINCED THEM NOW THAT THERE *IS* LIFE *ON* THE EARTH! IN FACT, THEY'RE READY TO HELP ME CONQUER THE HUMANS UP THERE! BUT FIRST--

8

-- I MUST ELIMINATE MY MOST DANGEROUS FOES-- *SOLOVAR, GORILLA-CITY,* AND THE *FLASH!* THIS *DEVOLUTIONIZER RAY* WILL REVERT THE SUPER-GORILLAS TO PRIMITIVE PRIMATES-- NO DIFFERENT FROM THE OTHER DUMB GORILLAS OF EARTH!

STORY CONTINUES ON FOLLOWING PAGE!

THE **METAL BORERS** THAT THE BIRD-PEOPLE SHOT UP INTO THE EARTH AT MY DIRECTION WERE JUST DEVICES TO DISTRACT **SOLOVAR** AND HIS ASSISTANTS FROM MY REAL THREAT-- AGAINST **THEM**!

ANOTHER FEW SECONDS AND IT WILL BE TIME TO SEND **SOLOVAR** AND HIS GORILLAS INTO THEIR MONKEY PAST--AND BEGIN MY WAR AGAINST HUMANITY!

AT THAT MOMENT, DIRECTLY ABOVE ON EARTH...

FLASH! GRODD'S VIBRATIONARY-TRAIL HAS JUST BEEN DISCOVERED-- LEADING BELOW THE EARTH!

BELOW THE EARTH!?

YES-- STRAIGHT DOWN!

I'M GOING AFTER HIM, **SOLOVAR**!

SO FAST DOES THE **SCARLET SPEEDSTER** SPIN HIMSELF AROUND...

...THAT THE PARTICLES OF HIS BODY SLIP BETWEEN THE ATOMS OF THE SOLID EARTH...

...ENABLING HIM TO PENETRATE THE EARTH'S CRUST IN A TWINKLING...

BELOW THE EARTH'S CRUST-- A HOLLOW WORLD!

9

A MOMENTARY SEARCH REVEALS...

GRODD!

FLASH-- MY NEMESIS! I FORESAW THE POSSIBILITY HE MIGHT TRY TO STOP ME... HE'S IN FOR A STARTLING SURPRISE!

AS THE WORLD'S FASTEST HUMAN PUTS ON AN EXTRA BURST OF SPEED...

LOOKS LIKE GRODD HASN'T HAD TIME TO DO ANY REAL HARM YET! THIS IS MY CHANCE TO GRAB HIM BEFORE HE CAN GET STARTED!

BUT AS FLASH HURTLES ACROSS THE INTERVENING SPACE, A STRANGE PROCESS TAKES PLACE...

WHAT'S...

...HAPPENING...

...TO ME?..

JUST AS MY EXPERIMENTS PROVED! FLASH'S SUPER-SPEED IS CAUSING THE MOLA--THE STRANGE AIR DOWN HERE--TO ADHERE TO HIS BODY-- AND INSTANTLY SOLIDIFY HIM!

BY PLUTO! HE'S STILL ADVANCING--EVEN THOUGH HIS WEIGHT HAS INCREASED A HUNDREDFOLD! IT'S GOT TO STOP HIM!

AS THE GREAT-HEARTED SPEEDSTER FINALLY CRASHES TO A HALT...

THE MOLA FINALLY STOPPED HIM! BUT IN DOING SO--FLASH DAMAGED MY DEVOLUTIONIZER!

10

A WORLD OF WINGED PEOPLE WHO FLY FROM ONE ISLAND TO ANOTHER HERE BELOW THE EARTH!

IN HIS SEMI-SUSPENDED ANIMATION STATE, FLASH GRASPS THE SITUATION AROUND HIM...

FROM THE DAZED LOOK OF THESE BIRD PEOPLE, GRODD MUST HAVE THEM IN SOME KIND OF FORCE OF MIND TRANCE!

AND IT LOOKS AS IF THEY'RE READY TO HELP GRODD IN HIS MAD AMBITION TO CONQUER THE WORLD-- ABOVE AND BELOW!

I MUST GET OUT OF THIS--STOP GRODD! BUT... HOW?

I CAN'T MOVE A FINGER! BUT WAIT... MAYBE THERE IS ONE CHANCE! I CAN MOVE SLIGHTLY ON THIS PEDESTAL... THE SURFACE UNDER ME IS JUST A TRIFLE UNEVEN...

IF I CAN VIBRATE BACK AND FORTH ENOUGH... WORK UP A ROCKING MOTION... MIGHT BE ABLE TO TOPPLE MYSELF OFF THIS PEDESTAL!

12

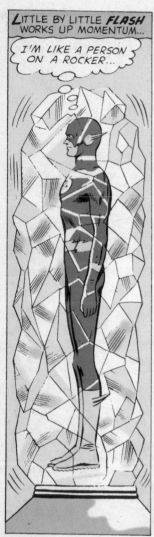

LITTLE BY LITTLE **FLASH** WORKS UP MOMENTUM...

I'M LIKE A PERSON ON A ROCKER...

...TRYING TO MAKE THE ROCKER TOPPLE OVER...

*BY ROCKING **HARD** ENOUGH.! ONCE MORE--!*

THEN... I'M ON THE EDGE... I'M GOING OVER.!

AS THE "HUMAN STATUE" HITS THE GROUND...

JUST AS I HOPED, THE CRYSTAL-LIKE MASS AROUND ME IS SHATTERING ON THE GROUND--

*--BUT IT'S LEFT ME UNHURT.! NOW, TO GET AFTER **GRODD** AGAIN--*

13

AT THAT MOMENT... AT LAST-- I'VE GOT MY **DEVOLUTIONIZER** IN WORKING ORDER AGAIN! TOO BAD I CAN'T BE UP THERE TO WATCH **SOLOVAR** TURN INTO A BABBLING GORILLA **AS I PRESS THIS LEVER--**

BEFORE THE **SUPER-GORILLA** CAN MAKE A MOVE...

FLASH-- AGAIN?

GOT TO CONTROL MY SPEED--KEEP IT JUST **UNDER** THE CRITICAL POINT WHERE IT WILL SOLIDIFY THIS ATMOSPHERE AROUND ME!

AS THE HUMAN COMET THROWS A WHORL OF AIR MOVING AT TORNADO SPEED AROUND HIS FOE...

AHH!

THAT SHOULD HOLD HIM!

BUT THE NEXT MOMENT, AMAZINGLY...

HIS STRENGTH IS... FANTASTIC! HE BURST OUT OF THE WHIRLWIND I CAUSED AROUND HIM! NO ONE'S EVER DONE THAT BEFORE!

YOU WON'T STOP **ME**, **FLASH**!

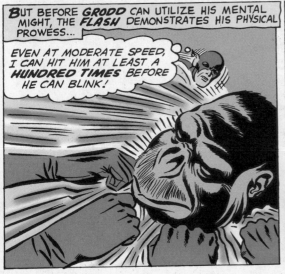

BUT BEFORE **GRODD** CAN UTILIZE HIS MENTAL MIGHT, THE **FLASH** DEMONSTRATES HIS PHYSICAL PROWESS...

EVEN AT MODERATE SPEED, I CAN HIT HIM AT LEAST A **HUNDRED TIMES** BEFORE HE CAN BLINK!

AND WHEN THE FLURRY OF ACTION IS OVER...

MAYBE **THAT** KNOCKED THE **FORCE OF MIND** POWER FROM HIM! I HOPE IT DID! AT LEAST... HE HAD NO CHANCE TO USE IT AGAINST ME--!

14

LATER...

YES...*GRODD* HAD US IN SOME KIND OF *SPELL!* BUT WHEN YOU KNOCKED HIM OUT, HIS HOLD ON US WAS BROKEN! WE'RE FREE NOW!

AS THE *FASTEST HUMAN* AND HIS CAPTIVE ZOOM BACK TOWARD THE SURFACE...

THE BIRD-PEOPLE ARE PEACEFUL! SOMEDAY WHEN THEY ARE READY THEY WILL PAY A VISIT TO THE SURFACE! UNTIL THEN, PERHAPS IT WOULD BE BEST FOR ME NOT TO SAY ANYTHING ABOUT THEIR SUBTERRANEAN EXISTENCE!

IN *GORILLA-CITY* SOON AFTER...

WE'LL BE MORE CAREFUL ABOUT WATCHING *GRODD* THIS TIME, *FLASH!* THANKS FOR CAPTURING HIM AGAIN!

GOODBYE, *SOLOVAR!* TIME FOR ME TO RETURN HOME...

15

AS BARRY "*FLASH*" ALLEN READS THE PAPERS LATER...

I SEE THAT THE "STRANGE METAL OBJECTS" VANISHED AS MYSTERIOUSLY AS THEY APPEARED! I HOPE THAT'S THE LAST I EVER HEAR OF THE EVIL-MINDED *GRODD!*

The End

BUT THE *FLASH'S* HOPE IS DUE TO RECEIVE AN ELECTRIFYING JOLT WHEN THE *SUPER-GORILLA* MAKES A STARTLING REAPPEARANCE! WATCH FOR IT IN A FORTHCOMING ISSUE OF...

THE *FLASH!*

AS THE FLASH SPEEDS HOMEWARD AFTER HAVING SUCCESSFULLY COMPLETED A CASE...

GREAT SCOTT! THAT TRUCK-- THE DRIVER MUST HAVE PARKED IT THERE ON THAT HILL -IT'S STARTING TO ROLL DOWN!

IT WILL CRASH INTO THAT STORE--HURT PEOPLE UNLESS IT'S STOPPED! GOT TO REACH IT IN TIME!

BUT THEN, INCREDIBLY, AS THE FASTEST MAN ALIVE PUTS ON AN EXTRA BURST OF SPEED, ANOTHER FIGURE SHOOTS PAST HIM...

EH? I'M GOING AT SUPER-SPEED... BUT SOMEONE IS WHIZZING PAST ME AS IF I WAS STANDING STILL--!

IN LESS THAN A WINK...

HE STOPPED THE TRUCK! BUT--WHO CAN THAT BE? I MUST FIND OUT!

SCREECH!

BUT SECONDS LATER, A SURPRISE FOR FLASH...

WHAT? YOU SAY YOU DON'T KNOW WHO--

THAT'S RIGHT! I DON'T KNOW WHO I AM...

LATER, IN AN APARTMENT THAT *FLASH* KEEPS TO PROTECT HIS DUAL IDENTITY OF BARRY ALLEN, POLICE SCIENTIST...

I HAD TO BRING HIM HERE! I HAD TO FIND OUT ALL I COULD ABOUT A MAN WHO COULD *OUTSTRIP ME* IN SPEED!

AND YOU SAY THAT ALL YOU REMEMBER IS THAT EARLY THIS AFTERNOON YOU FOUND YOURSELF WANDERING ON THE OUTSKIRTS OF THE CITY?

THAT'S RIGHT, *FLASH*...

WHY, I DIDN'T EVEN KNOW *YOUR* NAME--UNTIL YOU TOLD IT TO ME A FEW MINUTES AGO!

IT'S A CLEAR CASE OF AMNESIA...

I'M GOING TO SEE THAT YOU GET THE BEST MEDICAL ATTENTION AS SOON AS POSSIBLE--TO HELP RECOVER YOUR MEMORY!

THANKS...

BUT UNKNOWN TO THE *SCARLET SPEEDSTER* AT THIS MOMENT...

...AND EYE-WITNESSES SAY THE *STRANGER* SPRINTED RIGHT PAST THE *FLASH*! DO YOU REALIZE WHAT THAT MEANS, CHIEF?

ER--NOT QUITE, IRIS!

AS IRIS WEST, OF *PICTURE NEWS*, DETAILS AN ANGLE TO HER EDITOR...

THIS THING COULD BE BUILT UP AS A *TERRIFIC PUBLICITY STUNT!* EVERYONE BELIEVES *FLASH* IS THE *WORLD'S FASTEST HUMAN*--!

WHAT ARE YOU GETTING AT, IRIS?

LET'S ARRANGE A *RACE* BETWEEN THE TWO OF THEM -- SPONSORED BY *PICTURE NEWS* FOR CONSOLIDATED CHARITIES!

IT WILL SELL A MILLION EXTRA COPIES OF *PICTURE NEWS* -- AND BESIDES IT WILL SETTLE THE *QUESTION* -- WHO IS REALLY FASTER, *FLASH* OR THIS -- STRANGER!?

WONDERFUL! GO TO IT, IRIS!

SOON AFTER...

HMM! THIS LOOKS LIKE IRIS'S WORK ALL RIGHT...

PUBLIC OPINION MOUNTING FOR A RACE BETWEEN FLASH -- MYSTERIOUS STRANGER!

BUT I CAN'T AFFORD TO IGNORE IT! IF I DID, *FLASH'S* REPUTATION MIGHT SUFFER -- AND SO MIGHT HIS CRUSADE AGAINST CRIME!

LATER, AT A DOCTOR'S OFFICE...

THE DOCTOR HASN'T YET FOUND OUT WHAT'S WRONG WITH ME, *FLASH!*

WE'LL HAVE TO POSTPONE YOUR TREATMENTS...

DOCTOR

...UNTIL AFTER OUR *RACE*...IF YOU'RE WILLING...

I'LL DO WHATEVER YOU SAY, FLASH! I'M READY... TO *RACE!*

As the day of the great event dawns...

I DON'T GET IT, IRIS-- WHY IS THE *STRANGER* FACING THE STARTING LINE *BACKWARDS*?

I CAN EXPLAIN THAT, CHIEF--

IT WAS *MY* IDEA! I WATCHED THE *STRANGER* PRACTICE AND I BECAME CONVINCED HE COULD BEAT THE *FLASH* EVEN RUNNING BACKWARDS-- SO I TOLD HIM TO-- AND HE SAID HE WOULD!

IT'LL MAKE AN EVEN *BETTER* STORY THIS WAY--IF FLASH GETS BEATEN!

BANG!

THE STARTING GUN--THEY'RE OFF!

IN LESS TIME THAN IT TAKES TO DRAW A COUPLE OF BREATHS, THE TWO SPEEDSTERS HAVE ROUNDED THE FIELD AN INCREDIBLE *999* TIMES IN THE *1,000-LAP* RACE...

TOOK ME A SPLIT-SECOND TO BUILD UP SPEED--BUT HE *INSTANTLY* STARTED OFF AT HIGH SPEED-- AND IS MAINTAINING HIS SLIGHT LEAD!

GASP! HARD TO SEE... THEY MOVE SO FAST!

AS A HIGH-SPEED CAMERA RECORDS THE FINISH...

THE *STRANGER* WINS! BUT HE'S NOT FASTER THAN I--JUST TAKES OFF FASTER!

AFTER THE RACE...

NOW MORE THAN EVER I'VE *GOT* TO FIND OUT *WHO* HE IS--AND *WHERE* HE COMES FROM! I'M TAKING HIM *BACK TO THE DOCTOR*...

LATER...

WE'VE DECIDED TO USE *ELECTRIC* TREATMENTS TO JOG HIS MEMORY, *FLASH!*

I'M AGREEABLE--

SOON, WITH THE WIRES IN PLACE...

HERE GOES... I HOPE IT WORKS!

THEN, AFTER THE SURGING CURRENT HAS BEEN SHUT OFF...

I--I--

SPEAK! CAN YOU REMEMBER ANYTHING?

WHAT I HAVE TO SAY... I CAN SAY ONLY TO THE FLASH--*ALONE!!*

HUH?

OUTSIDE THE DOCTOR'S OFFICE, MOMENTS LATER...

FLASH, LISTEN-- I KNOW WHO I AM NOW! BUT I ALSO KNOW THAT **SOMETHING** HAS HAPPENED TO ME!

WHAT DO YOU MEAN?

WHEN THAT ELECTRICITY SURGED THROUGH ME IT NOT ONLY **BROUGHT BACK MY MEMORY**-- IT ALSO DESTROYED MY SPEED! I SENSED IT THE MOMENT IT HAPPENED--! TO PROVE IT--

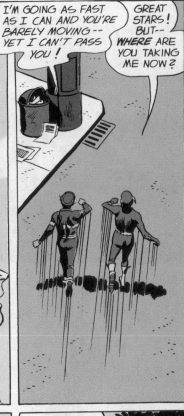

I'M GOING AS FAST AS I CAN AND YOU'RE BARELY MOVING-- YET I CAN'T PASS YOU!

GREAT STARS! BUT-- **WHERE** ARE YOU TAKING ME NOW?

I'LL SHOW YOU...ONE OF THE THINGS I REMEMBERED WAS **HOW** I CAME HERE TO YOUR PLANET! YOU SEE--I'M NOT OF YOUR WORLD, FLASH!

I CAME HERE BY SPACESHIP--BUT MY SHIP CRASHED! THE CRASH ROBBED ME OF MY MEMORY...

BUT NOW I KNOW THAT YOU MUST HELP ME...BY PERFORMING A TASK OF THE UTMOST URGENCY--!

WHAT TASK--?

Editor's Note: A HOMINOID IS A HUMAN-LIKE ROBOT!

"I KNEW MY JOB! I HAD PERFORMED IT MANY TIMES BEFORE..."

ON THE PLANETOID F203 NEAR THE CENTER OF THE GALAXY THERE IS A **WEAK SPOT**... WHERE THE TERRIBLE FORCES OF **ANOTHER DIMENSION** THREATEN TO **BREAK THROUGH!** EVERY FEW YEARS THE BARRIER HOLDING BACK THOSE FORCES...

...MUST BE REPAIRED OR THE GALAXY WILL BE DESTROYED! BUT NOW, WITHOUT MY SPEED, I CAN DO NOTHING! YOU MUST TAKE MY PLACE, **FLASH** -- YOU **MUST** REPAIR THE BARRIER! IT'LL BE A RACE AGAINST TIME!

SOON AFTER, CONDUCTED TO THE **WEAK SPOT** BY **KYRI**, FLASH GETS A GLIMPSE OF THE TITANIC FORCES IN THE DIMENSION BEYOND...

FANTASTIC! IT'S AS IF LIGHTNING IN A RIOT OF DIFFERENT COLORS WERE EXPLODING IN ALL DIRECTIONS!

THE HOLE IS WIDENING! YOU MUST SEAL IT AT ONCE, **FLASH!** HURRY--!

WHIRLING AROUND THE WEAK SPOT, THE **SCARLET SPEEDSTER'S** INCREDIBLE VELOCITY **MELTS** THE ROCKS AND MINERALS AROUND IT...

THESE ROCKS AND MINERALS...

...MUST BE MELTED IN EXACTLY THE RIGHT ORDER...

...SO THAT THEY **FUSE** TOGETHER TO MAKE A SUPER-COSMIC GLUE!

WHEN THE **MAN OF SUPER-SPEED** SLOWS DOWN AGAIN...

WONDERFUL, **FLASH!** YOU'VE SEALED OFF THE DANGER! NOW THE GALAXY IS SAFE--FOR SEVERAL MORE YEARS!

TIME FOR ME TO TAKE YOU HOME NOW, *FLASH*-- AND THEN RETURN MYSELF--TO MY MASTERS!

ON EARTH, SOON AFTER...

FAREWELL, FLASH...

GOODBY, KYRI--!

TO THINK...HE WASN'T HUMAN AFTER ALL-- ONLY AN ARTIFICIAL CREATURE--

WELL...THIS MEANS I AM STILL THE FASTEST MAN ALIVE--AT LEAST THE FASTEST TO BE FOUND IN NATURE!

AS THE *FLASH*, VISITING *PICTURE NEWS*, CORRECTS AN IMPRESSION...

GOLLY! THEN FROM WHAT YOU SAY, FLASH--YOU ARE *STILL* THE WORLD'S FASTEST *HUMAN*!

ER--**NATURALLY**, MISS WEST!

The End

30

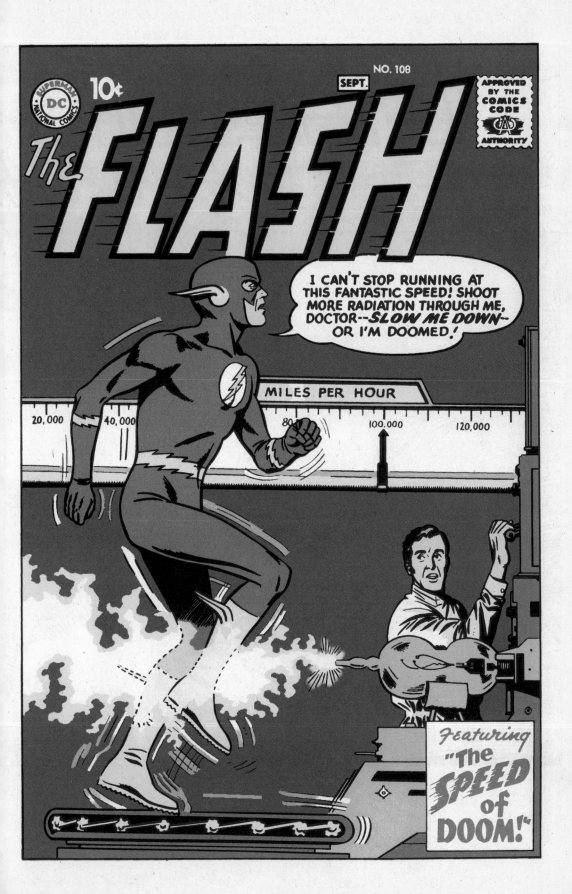

THE FLASH

The SPEED of DOOM!

EVEN THE LEGENDARY PROWESS OF THE *FASTEST MAN ALIVE* WAS HARD-PRESSED TO EQUAL THE INCREDIBLE SPEED OF THE *MOHRUVIANS*--MYSTERIOUS, UNEARTHLY CREATURES WHOSE SOLE PURPOSE ON EARTH WAS TO COLLECT OBJECTS STRUCK BY LIGHTNING! WHY? FOR WHAT SINISTER PURPOSE?

TWO OF THE LIGHTNING-FAST THIEVES RAN *INTO* THIS HILL AND *DISAPPEARED!* ONLY CHANCE OF SOLVING THIS MYSTERY IS TO GRAB THE THIRD ONE -- BEFORE HE DISAPPEARS TOO!

"TIME WAS RUNNING OUT ON ME! I STRUGGLED TO FREE MYSELF, BUT.."

GOING FASTER... FASTER! AND I CAN'T JUMP OFF HERE--THAT RADIATION IS KEEPING ME ON THIS TREADMILL TOO!

GETTING WEAKER! NO HUMAN BEING CAN KEEP GOING AT THIS KILLING PACE! BUT I MUST...KEEP FIGHTING... KEEP TRYING TO...SLOW DOWN...!

AND--ALTHOUGH FLASH DIDN'T KNOW IT AT THE TIME--EXTRA-ORDINARY EVENTS HAD COM-BINED TO BRING ABOUT HIS PERILOUS POSITION!

"IN THE LAND OF MOHRU NOT LONG BEFORE, IN THE OFFICE OF THE POLICE PREFECT..."

...AND THE RECENT RAIDS OF THE MYSTERY BAND OF THIEVES HAVE CAUSED HAVOC IN MOHRU!

WHY HAVEN'T WE BEEN ABLE TO APPREHEND THEM, SIR?

BECAUSE THEY HAVE DISCOVERED A WAY OF MOVING SO FAST THAT THEY BECOME INVISIBLE! OUR AGENTS HAVE BROUGHT US MUCH INFORMATION ABOUT THIS INCREDIBLE GANG...

"FOR ONE THING, THEY HAVE FOUND A WAY OF GETTING INTO THE NEARBY DIMENSIONAL WORLD OF EARTH!"

HA! HA! TIME TO BRING SOME MORE SPEED-MAKERS BACK FROM EARTH TO MY OWN WORLD OF MOHRLI!

WHAT WE HAVEN'T BEEN ABLE TO FIND OUT IS WHAT THESE "SPEEDMAKERS" ARE! THEY GO INTO EARTH TO FIND SOMETHING...

SOMETHING THAT GIVES THEM THE POWER TO MOVE AT INCREDIBLE SPEED -- AND ELUDE ALL EFFORTS OF OUR POLICE TO CATCH THEM! BUT WHAT IT COULD BE, WE HAVE NO IDEA!

THE MOHRLI POLICE KNEW PART OF THE STORY... BUT IT WAS FLASH WHO FOUND OUT THE MOST IMPORTANT PART!! I'LL NEVER FORGET THE WAY IT ALL CAME ABOUT...

"I WAS STILL TRAPPED ON THE SPEEDING MACHINE.."

CAN'T GO ON MUCH LONGER-- BUT-- I JUST THOUGHT OF SOMETHING --

MILES PER HOUR
90,000   100,000

I'VE BEEN TRYING TO SLOW MYSELF DOWN TO ESCAPE THIS TRAP! WHAT IF-- I TRY TO GO FASTER-- UP TO MY MAXIMUM SPEED!?

MILES PE

100,00

*EDITOR'S NOTE: A FULGURITE IS FUSED SAND OR ROCK FORMED BY THE ACTION OF LIGHTNING!

ONLY ONE THING TO DO! THEY WERE TRAVELING FAST--AND WHEN THEY STRUCK THE HILLSIDE AT A CERTAIN POINT--THEY DISAPPEARED! I'M GOING TO TRY THE *SAME* THING!

"STEPPING UP MY SPEED TO MATCH THAT OF THE DISAPPEARING THIEVES, I DASHED AT THE HILL AND...

BREAKING THROUGH--INTO SOME *OTHER WORLD*-- AND THERE ARE THE THIEVES!

THE *FLASH!* HE-- ESCAPED FROM OUR *TRAP!*

THERE'S THE *PHONY* DR. HIRACH! I RECOGNIZE HIM!

FLEE!

CAN'T LET THEM ESCAPE--!

"WHIRLING PAST MY FOES AT SUPER-SPEED, I TURNED THEM ALL INTO SPINNING TOPS..."

THIS...WILL TAKE SOME...

OF THE EXTRA ENERGY...

OUT OF THESE FAST-MOVING THIEVES!

THE FLASH

The SUPER-GORILLA'S SECRET IDENTITY!

THE STRANGEST ARMY IMAGINABLE WAS POISED TO STRIKE A SHATTERING BLOW AT THE EARTH! IN COMMAND WAS GRODD, A POWER-MAD GORILLA WITH THE MIND OF A GENIUS! ONLY ONE MAN HAD A CHANCE OF STOPPING GRODD'S CONQUEST OF EARTH-- THE FLASH-- BUT TO SUCCEED, THE FASTEST MAN ALIVE HAD TO DISCOVER...

TREES-- I COMMAND YOU-- UPROOT YOUR-SELVES-- STRIKE AT THE FLASH!

GREAT THUNDER! SO THAT'S GRODD'S SECRET WEAPON-- THE POWER OF MIND OVER MATTER!

IN DEEPEST AFRICA, SHIELDED FROM HUMAN SENSES, LIES *GORILLA-CITY*, STRONGHOLD OF A SUPER-SCIENTIFIC CIVILIZATION...

IMPRISONED IN A *GORILLA-CITY* CELL IS *GRODD*, THE EVIL GORILLA GENIUS WHOSE PLANS TO GAIN CONTROL OF THE EARTH HAVE TWICE BEEN THWARTED BY THE *FLASH*...*

THE FIRST TIME I WAS CAUGHT, THEY HAD *ONE* GUARD WATCHING ME-- AND I ESCAPED! NOW THERE ARE FOUR GUARDS --AND I'LL STILL BREAK OUT OF HERE!

*Editor's Note: AS RECORDED IN THE TWO PREVIOUS ISSUES OF THIS MAGAZINE!

I FORESAW THE POSSIBILITY OF MY RECAPTURE... SO PREPARED AN *ESCAPE*... WHICH I SHALL NOW PROCEED TO CARRY OUT!

A THOUGHT-IMPULSE FROM *GRODD'S* MIND IS BEAMED AT A HIDDEN *QUADROMOBILE*-- A REMARKABLE FOUR-WAY VEHICLE THAT TRAVELS THROUGH THE AIR, ON THE GROUND, UNDER WATER, AND THROUGH THE EARTH...

ONLY MY THOUGHTS ARE ATTUNED TO THE CONTROLS OF THE QUADROMOBILE!

QUADROMOBILE -- FOLLOW MY THOUGHT-- IMPULSES-- COME TO ME...

INSTANTLY...

ZIP!

THE FOLLOWING MOMENT...

FULL SPEED -- RIGHT THROUGH THE CELL WALL -- NOW STOP!

IN THE CONFUSION... THIS WILL TEACH CHIEF SOLOVAR AND HIS GORILLA-MINIONS THAT NO PRISON OF THEIRS CAN HOLD ME!

LIKE A FAST-AS-LIGHT MISSILE, THE QUADRO-MOBILE SHOOTS SKYWARD...

HA HA...

OVER MID-OCEAN GRODD'S INCREDIBLE CRAFT DARTS DOWN-WARD...

NOW TO CARRY OUT THE NEXT PHASE OF MY PREPARED PLAN...

...ACTIVATE MY EVOLUTION-ACCELERATOR! THIS INVENTION OF MY SUPER-BRAIN WILL ADVANCE ME FAR ALONG THE EVOLUTIONARY TRACK--

--THE NEXT STEP AFTER MODERN MAN!

NOT LONG AFTERWARD IN THE STREETS OF *CENTRAL CITY*...

FOUR WEEKS SINCE *SOLOVAR* CONTACTED *FLASH* AND INFORMED HIM OF *GRODD'S* ESCAPE! AND *STILL* NO SIGN OF HIM --

BUT I *CAN'T* WORRY ABOUT THAT *MAD GORILLA* NOW! I'VE GOT A DATE WITH *IRIS* -- AND I'D BETTER NOT BE LATE *AGAIN*!

BUT AS POLICE SCIENTIST *BARRY ALLEN* -- ALIAS *THE FLASH* -- HURRIES ALONG...

GREAT SCOTT! SOMETHING'S HAPPENED TO THAT CRANE! THE BOOM IS FALLING -- RIGHT OVER *IRIS*!

WRIGHT
CTION

IN A SPLIT-INSTANT DECISION, A SPURT OF RED SHOOTS FROM THE RING ON BARRY'S FINGER...

OUT OF THE BLUR OF MOTION A FIGURE PLUNGES...

THE FLASH!

AS THE *SCARLET SPEEDSTER* STRAINS TO REACH HIS TOP SPEED...

IT'S ALMOST ON HER! A SPLIT-SECOND LEFT TO REACH HER!

THEN... Made it!

Bodily lifted by a tremendous gust of wind--!

CRASH!

WHEN THE **HUMAN COMET** RELEASES HIS HOLD ON IRIS...

FLASH, IT WAS **YOU**! I DON'T KNOW **HOW** YOU MANAGED TO BE HERE IN THE NICK OF TIME--BUT I'VE GOT TO TALK TO YOU--!

ER--LATER, MISS WEST! I HAVE A-- ER--PREVIOUS APPOINTMENT!

AS THE **FASTEST MAN ALIVE** DARTS INTO AN ALLEYWAY...

WHAT COULD IRIS WANT TO SPEAK TO **FLASH** ABOUT, I WONDER?... MAYBE **BARRY ALLEN** CAN FIND OUT--!

MOMENTS LATER...

HI, IRIS!

BARRY! IF YOU HADN'T BEEN **LATE AGAIN**, MAYBE **YOU** COULD HAVE BEEN A HERO AND SAVED ME--INSTEAD OF **FLASH**!

AS BARRY SOUNDS OUT IRIS AT LUNCH...

...AND AS YOU KNOW, BARRY, EACH YEAR MY NEWSPAPER **PICTURE NEWS** NAMES A **MAN OF THE YEAR**! UP TO FOUR WEEKS AGO, **FLASH** WAS A SHOO-IN TO WIN! THAT'S WHEN A "**DARK HORSE**" CANDIDATE APPEARED--

--IN THE PERSON OF **DREW DROWDEN**--WHO DRAMATICALLY CAPTURED THE IMAGINATION OF THE COUNTRY! WHY, THINK OF IT, BARRY--JUST A MONTH AGO NO ONE HAD EVER HEARD OF HIM--

"HE APPEARED OUT OF NOWHERE..."

"BUT EVEN THEN HIS IMPOSING APPEARANCE--SO BIG AND STRONG--STRUCK EVERY EYE!"

"AND THEN WITHIN **ONE WEEK** ON THE STOCK MARKET..."

MR. DROWDEN, REPORTS SAY YOU'VE MADE **MILLIONS** ON THE EXCHANGE! IS THAT TRUE?

IT IS!

BUT **HOW?** DO YOU HAVE A SYSTEM?

NOT REALLY! SIMPLY INFORM THE PUBLIC I DID IT WITH MY **SUPERIOR MENTAL POWERS!**

"AND THEN, WHAT DOES DROWDEN DO WITH HIS FORTUNE, BARRY? HE BUILDS A HUGE **FACTORY** WITH HUNDREDS OF WORKERS... ON ACRES OF LAND! AND--MOST INCREDIBLE--NO ONE EVEN KNOWS WHAT THE FACTORY IS FOR...!"

AT LAST THE FACTORY'S FINISHED! NOW TO GET THINGS RUNNING--SO THAT I CAN FULFILL MY AMBITION--THE **GREATEST** AMBITION ANYONE EVER DREAMED OF!

SO...WILL FLASH BE NAMED MAN OF THE YEAR -- OR DROWDEN? RIGHT NOW IT'S A TOSSUP--AND WILL DEPEND ON WHAT EACH DOES BEFORE OUR PAPER'S DEADLINE NEXT WEEK!

WELL, I'LL--ER--BE ROOTING FOR THE FLASH!

LATER, AFTER LUNCH, AS THE TWO SEPARATE...

OH, WHY COULDN'T IT BE BARRY WHO'S THE MAN OF THE YEAR!? (sigh...)

MEANWHILE, AT DROWDEN'S MYSTERIOUS FACTORY...

AT LAST... THE RESULT OF THE LABOR OF HUN-DREDS OF TRAINED TECHNICIANS -- FOR WEEKS! THIS PILL...

IT IS THE END-PRODUCT OF THE COMBINED EFFORT HERE -- AND WHAT IS MORE, NOT A SINGLE MAN HAS THE SLIGHTEST INKLING OF WHAT HIS WORK HAS LED UP TO!

ONLY I KNOW THAT THIS PILL WILL MAKE ME THE MOST POWERFUL INDIVIDUAL IN THE WORLD!

LATER, AFTER THE LAST WORKMAN HAS LEFT THE FACTORY...

NOW... TO SEE HOW WELL THE PILL WORKS!

TREE... COME TOWARD ME! TREE... I COMMAND YOU--

THE NEXT MOMENT, THE TREE STUMBLINGLY ADVANCES TOWARD DROWDEN...

IT'S WORKING!
IT'S WORKING!

TREE-- STOP!

YES, I HAVE DONE IT! I HAVE GAINED THE POWER OF MIND OVER MATTER!

DROWDEN'S FOLLOW-UP COMMAND FORCES A LINE OF TREES TO UPROOT THEMSELVES AND FLY INTO THE AIR...

NOW I HAVE THE POWER TO CONQUER THE WORLD! AND FOR MY ARMY-- I SHALL USE TREES, MOUNTAINS, RIVERS--ALL THE FORCES OF NATURE WILL BE UNDER MY COMMAND!

NOTHING WILL BE ABLE TO STOP THEM-- OR ME!!

story continues on following page! 8

As a crimson streak darts across the horizon near **CENTRAL CITY**...

STRANGE! A REPORT-- OVER THE POLICE RADIO--

--OF TREES SEEN SHOOTING UP INTO THE AIR NEAR THE **DROWDEN FACTORY**!

SOUNDS LIKE SOMETHING THAT **FLASH** BETTER HAVE A LOOK INTO-- RIGHT AWAY!

AT THAT MOMENT, **DROWDEN'S** MIND-OVER-MATTER POWER IS RECEIVING ANOTHER TEST...

WITH HARDLY ANY EFFORT, I LIFTED MY FACTORY OFF THE EARTH--MADE IT SPIN AROUND..!

JUST AS THE FACTORY IS "GROUNDED"...

THERE'S **DROWDEN**-- I RECOGNIZE HIM FROM HIS NEWS PICTURES! BUT-- WHAT'S HE DOING?

FLASH--!?

I'VE GOT TO FIND OUT WHAT HE'S UP TO!

THIS IS **ONE TIME** MY NEMESIS THE **FLASH** IS NOT GOING TO UPSET MY PLANS! I'LL STOP HIM WITH THE **FINGERS OF DOOM**!

AND AS THE **FASTEST MAN ALIVE** STRIVES TO REACH THE **MYSTERY MAN**...

WHAT'S WRONG? I'M SLOWING DOWN--!

I KNEW THE FLASH WOULD BE NO MATCH FOR ME!

9

AND AS *FLASH* STARES AGHAST...

INCREDIBLE--!! *DREW DROWDEN*--CHANGING INTO--

GRODD--THE *EVIL SUPER-GORILLA!* NO WONDER WE COULDN'T FIND ANY TRACE OF HIM!

YOU'LL NEVER REVEAL MY SECRET, *FLASH!*

BUT THIS TIME, WHEN *GRODD* POINTS HIS FINGER AT HIS FOE...

I CAN MOVE AGAIN!

MY POWER-- IT'S *GONE!*

IT'S ONLY AS A *HUMAN* THAT I HAVE THE MIND-OVER-MATTER POWER-- BECAUSE AS A *HUMAN* MY BRAIN IS ON A HIGHER EVOLUTIONARY LEVEL! MY GORILLA BRAIN CAN'T USE THE POWER!

GOT TO REACH MY *EVOLUTION-ACCELERATOR!* TURN IT ON-- MAKE ME *HUMAN* AGAIN!

BUT AS THE *SCARLET SPEEDSTER* SEEKS TO SEIZE HIS FOE, A WHIRL OF POWERFUL SHOULDERS SENDS HIM FLYING...

I'VE STILL GOT MY *SUPER-GORILLA* STRENGTH, *FLASH!* YOU'LL NEVER CAPTURE ME!

RACING INTO A SPECIAL ROOM IN THE FACTORY...

THE EVOLUTIONARY CHANGE ONLY TAKES A SECOND OR TWO--

WHAT'S THAT MYSTERIOUS-LOOKING MACHINE!? MUST BE A WEAPON HE'S GOING TO USE AGAINST ME!

STREAKING ACROSS THE HUGE ROOM, THE *WORLD'S FASTEST HUMAN* GOES SO RAPIDLY THAT HE IGNITES THE OXYGEN IN THE AIR AS HE PASSES...

HE'S REACHING FOR THE SWITCH! I'LL NEED AN EXTRA BURST OF SPEED TO STOP HIM!

AT *SUPER-SPEED, FLASH* CRASHES INTO HIS 500-POUND FOE...

HIT HIM-- WITH PILE-DRIVER FORCE!

THEN...

STILL STANDING?! AN IRRESISTIBLE FORCE MEETING AN IMMOVABLE OBJECT--!

/12

I'VE CHANGED MY MIND, *FLASH!* I'LL ENJOY MY TRIUMPH MORE BY ELIMINATING YOU IN MY *GORILLA-FORM!*

AFTER THAT, AS *DREW DROWDEN*-- WITH ABSOLUTE CONTROL OF MIND OVER MATTER--I SHALL RULE THE WORLD!

THEN THE FATE OF THE WORLD RESTS IN MY HANDS-- *HANDS!* THAT'S IT! I KNOW HOW TO STOP HIM!

AS THE *FASTEST MAN ALIVE* FOLLOWS THROUGH WITH HIS IDEA...

IF *YOU* WON'T USE YOUR MACHINE, *GRODD*-- I WILL!

BACK AND FORTH OVER THE MACHINE RUB THE *FLASH'S* HANDS-- SO FAST THAT THE FRICTION-HEAT CAUSES THE METAL TO MELT...

MY EVOLUTION-ACCELERATOR-- WHAT'S HE DOING TO IT?

THE NEXT MOMENT, AS THE EVIL ANTHROPOID TRIES TO INTERCEPT THE *SCARLET SPEEDSTER*...

THERE! THAT'LL HOLD YOU!

UH--! HANDCUFFED!

KLIK!

AS THE HUGE GORILLA STRAINS HELPLESSLY...

YOU'RE FINISHED, *GRODD!* THOSE HANDCUFFS--FASHIONED OUT OF THE METAL YOU MADE YOURSELF--ARE TOO STRONG FOR YOU TO BREAK!

13

THEN, WITH *FLASH* SUPPLYING THE POWER, THE SUPER-GORILLA "ROCKETS" HOME...

YOU'RE GOING BACK, GRODD -- TO GORILLA-CITY--

--BACK TO THE JAIL WHERE YOU BELONG! AND THIS TIME WE'LL MAKE SURE YOU DON'T ESCAPE AGAIN!

A WEEK LATER, IN A *CENTRAL CITY* DINING ROOM...

WELL, BARRY, YOU ROOTED HOME A WINNER -- *FLASH* HAS BEEN NAMED *MAN OF THE YEAR!* BUT WHAT MADE YOU SO CONFIDENT IT WOULDN'T BE *DREW DROWDEN?*

PICTURE NEWS
FLASH!
MAN OF THE YEAR!

IN A CLOSE RACE, YOU CAN ALWAYS RELY ON *FLASH* PUTTING ON AN EXTRA BURST OF SPEED TO WIN!

YOU'RE SO RIGHT!

The End

14

WATCH FOR THE NEXT EXCITING DUEL BETWEEN THE *FASTEST MAN ALIVE* AND THE *SUPER-GORILLA* IN A FORTH-COMING ISSUE OF *THE FLASH!*

IN THE *CENTRAL CITY PENITENTIARY*...

BLOCK 3

OKAY, HANK-- THE *WARDEN* HAS GIVEN US PERMISSION TO PHOTOGRAPH *SCUDDER!*

GOOD! I'M ALL SET, IRIS...

AS *IRIS WEST*-- CRACK REPORTER FOR *PICTURE NEWS*-- AND HER PHOTOGRAPHER PREPARE TO DO A STORY...

SCUDDER WAS KNOWN AS THE *MIRROR-MASTER* BEFORE *FLASH* CAUGHT UP WITH HIM! WE'LL GET A FRONT-PAGE SPREAD WITH A PICTURE OF SCUDDER BEHIND BARS!

SMILE AT THE BIRDIE, SCUDDER!

SMILE? I'LL DO MORE THAN THAT! I'LL *LAUGH*--AT WHAT'S GOING TO HAPPEN NEXT!

THE *FLASHBULB* GOES OFF...

THE NEXT MOMENT...

HEY, WHAT'S HAPPENED TO SCUDDER?!

HE--HE'S *DISAPPEARED!*

AS A MYSTERY MY ESCAPE HAS CREATED A SENSATION! BUT ACTUALLY IT WAS VERY SIMPLE-- FOR SOMEONE WHO CAN HANDLE *MIRRORS* THE WAY I CAN!

I HAD TINY MIRRORS CLEVERLY SECRETED ON MY PERSON WHEN THEY PUT ME IN JAIL! I COULD HAVE PULLED AN ESCAPE IMMEDIATELY-- BUT I WANTED THE RIGHT MOMENT! I GUESS I HAVE MY VANITY...

BY ARRANGING CERTAIN MIRRORS A CERTAIN WAY, A PERSON CAN BE INCREASED OR DECREASED IN SIZE! IT'S NOT DIFFICULT--IF YOU HAVE MY "MAGIC" MIRRORS TO WORK WITH!

"I LEARNED ABOUT MIRRORS THE FIRST TIME I WAS IN JAIL! ONE DAY IN THE PRISON WORKSHOP..."

SCUDDER, YOU'RE A WASH-OUT! YOU'VE RUINED THIS MIRROR! HERE, TAKE IT AND THROW IT OUT--!

"AS I TOOK THE MIRROR FROM TYLER'S HAND..."

THIS ISN'T MY FACE! IT'S TYLER'S-- THE FOREMAN'S! SOMEHOW THIS "RUINED" MIRROR HAS HELD TYLER'S IMAGE!

"I KNEW I'D MADE A STARTLING DISCOVERY..."

I HID THE MIRROR-- EXAMINED IT LATER AND DISCOVERED ITS SECRET! THAT WAS THE START OF MY AMAZING MIRROR DISCOVERIES!*

*EDITOR'S NOTE: A COMPLETE ACCOUNT OF THIS STORY APPEARS IN THE FEBRUARY- MARCH, 1959 ISSUE OF THIS MAGAZINE!

④

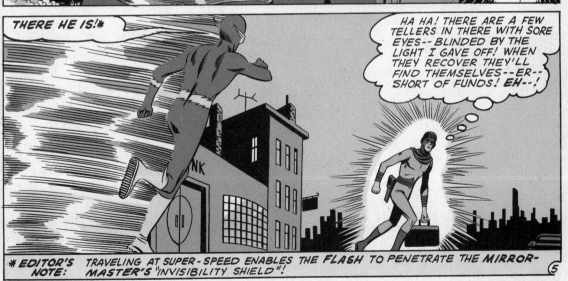

MEANWHILE, ON A ROOFTOP OF A *CENTRAL CITY* BUILDING...

I HAVE DECIDED I *MUST* GET RID OF *FLASH!* HE IS A *THORN* IN MY SIDE-- AND I'LL NEVER FEEL SAFE UNTIL I'VE *ERASED* HIM FROM THE SCENE!

BELOW IN THE CITY, SHORTLY AFTER...

GREAT SCOTT! A BLINDING LIGHT FROM UP ON THAT ROOF--!? THAT *COULD* BE THE *MIRROR-MASTER* AT WORK--!

INSTANTLY A RED SPLASH ERUPTS FROM THE RING ON BARRY ALLEN'S FINGER...

... A SPLASH OF RED THAT QUICKLY EXPANDS IN THE AIR TO BECOME GARMENTS...THE UNIFORM OF THE *FLASH, FASTEST MAN ALIVE!*

AND IN LESS THAN A WINK OF TIME...

A STRANGE MIRROR UP HERE! JUST AS I SUSPECTED! WHAT TRICKY MANEUVER IS THE *MIRROR-MASTER* PLANNING NOW?

HA HA! DREW THE *FLASH* TO ME--LIKE A MOTH TO A FLAME!

FLASH DOESN'T REALIZE IT--BUT THAT MIRROR HE'S LOOKING AT IS A *DECOY!* IT'S THIS *MIRROR-REDUCER* I'M DIRECTING AT HIM NOW THAT HE SHOULD BE ON HIS GUARD AGAINST! BUT IT'S *TOO LATE*...!

AS THE LIGHT FROM THE AMAZING MIRROR STRIKES *FLASH*, IT INSTANTLY *REDUCES HIM IN SIZE...!*

SMALLER...

AND EVEN SMALLER--ALL IN THE BLINK OF AN EYE...

HA HA! THAT'S HOW I ESCAPED FROM JAIL--BY MAKING MYSELF SO SMALL THAT I WALKED OUT WITHOUT BEING SEEN! BUT NOW LET'S SEE IF *FLASH* CAN ESCAPE MY VENGEANCE!

AS THE *MASTER OF MIRRORS* LUNGES AT HIS MINIATURE FOE...

TRYING TO AVOID ME--HE'S TOPPLING OFF THE ROOF! *THIS* IS THE *END* OF *FLASH* NOW!

BUT WHAT THE *MASTER OF MIRRORS* FAILS TO REALIZE...

THIS FALL WON'T HURT ME! I'M SMALLER THAN A MOUSE-- AND A MOUSE CAN FALL FROM EVEN A GREATER HEIGHT WITHOUT HARM!*

*EDITOR'S NOTE: IT IS A FACT THAT TINY ANIMALS CAN FALL FROM GREAT HEIGHTS WITHOUT INJURY! THIS IS BECAUSE OF THEIR SLIGHT WEIGHT AND THE BUOYANCY OF THE AIR!

ON THE SIDEWALK SOON...

I SURVIVED THAT FALL...BUT I'M STILL IN TERRIBLE DANGER! ONE OF THESE PASSERSBY MAY *STEP ON* ME!

AS THE IMPERILED *FLASH* DECIDES ON A COURSE OF ACTION...

I MUST GET TO THE POLICE LABORATORY! THERE I MAY BE ABLE TO GET MYSELF BACK TO MY PROPER SIZE--BY MEANS OF CERTAIN *RADIATION* THAT I KNOW *PROMOTES GROWTH!* FORTUNATELY I CAN STILL MOVE AT SUPER-SPEED EVEN IN MY REDUCED SIZE!

BUT THEN SUDDENLY...

EH? THAT MAN -- HE DOESN'T SEE THE CAR SPEEDING FROM BEHIND THAT PARKED TRUCK! IT WILL HIT HIM --

WITH THE FORCE OF A TORNADO, THE TINY FLASH HURTLES AT THE PEDESTRIAN...

OOF!

ONLY AN EXTRA BURST OF SPEED ENABLED ME TO MAKE A RUNNING BROAD JUMP OF THIS EXTENT!

G-GOLLY! SOMETHING SMACKED INTO ME AND SAVED ME FROM BEING RUN DOWN BY THAT CAR! BUT WHAT WAS IT? I DIDN'T SEE ANYTHING!

LATER, AT THE POLICE SCIENTIFIC DETECTION BUREAU WHERE BARRY ALLEN IS EMPLOYED...

MANAGED TO GET IN HERE ALL RIGHT! NOW FOR THE NEXT STEP...

I'VE GOT TO TURN ON THIS POLAROID LIGHT MACHINE! MY EXPERIMENTS SHOWED ITS RAYS INCREASE THE GROWTH OF CELLS AND PLANTS -- AND IT JUST MIGHT WORK ON ME!

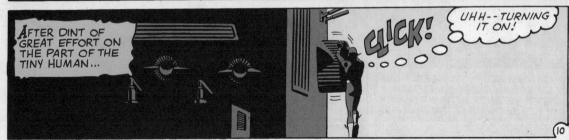

AFTER DINT OF GREAT EFFORT ON THE PART OF THE TINY HUMAN...

CLICK!

UHH -- TURNING IT ON!

10

MOMENTS LATER, AFTER AN INITIAL DISAPPOINTMENT...

IT DIDN'T WORK AT FIRST...

BUT IT *IS* WORKING NOW!

GETTING BIGGER-- BIGGER--

THEN...

WHEW! I'M *NORMAL* AGAIN! BUT NO TIME TO WASTE! IF I'M RIGHT, I KNOW WHERE TO FIND THE *MIRROR-MASTER* -- RIGHT *NOW!*

MEANWHILE, IN THE *CENTRAL CITY BANK,* AFTER HOURS...

HA HA! IT WAS CHILD'S PLAY TO MAKE MYSELF SMALL ENOUGH BY MY *MIRRORS* TO SLIP IN HERE UNDER THE DOOR-- AND THEN LARGE ENOUGH AGAIN TO TAKE THIS MONEY!

AS THE *MIRROR-MASTER* HEADS FOR THE EXIT...

F-FLASH! NOT AGAIN?!

I FIGURED YOU'D BE HERE, *MIRROR-MASTER!* THEY SAY A CRIMINAL ALWAYS RETURNS TO THE SCENE OF HIS CRIME...

*EDITOR'S NOTE: JUST AS A TORNADO-DRIVEN STRAW CAN PENETRATE SEVERAL FEET OF SOLID OAK, SO CAN *FLASH* AT SUPER-SPEED PENETRATE SOLID WALLS!

AND I FIGURED *YOU* WOULD NEVER REST UNTIL YOU RETURNED TO THIS SCENE OF YOUR UNSUCCESSFUL CRIME-- AND REDEEMED YOURSELF!

UHH!

11

THIS CARPET MAKES A CONVENIENT WAY TO KEEP THIS THIEF FROM USING HIS *MIRRORS!* AND THIS TIME IN JAIL I'LL MAKE SURE HE *NEVER* ESCAPES AGAIN!

WITH HIS FOE BEHIND BARS ONCE MORE, *BARRY ALLEN* HAS TIME FOR A PERSONAL PROBLEM...

IN THE HIDEOUT OF THE *MIRROR-MASTER,* AFTER HE WENT TO JAIL, I FOUND ALL THESE MIRROR-GADGETS OF HIS! AND I WONDER...IF I CAN'T *USE* ONE OF THEM MYSELF--IN AN *INNOCENT* WAY, OF COURSE!

IRIS *STILL* WON'T SPEAK TO ME! BUT MAYBE I CAN GET HER TO CHANGE HER MIND-- WITH THIS AMAZING *IMAGE-PROJECTOR!*

AND SOON, NEAR THE *PICTURE NEWS* BUILDING...

HMM! IT'S *BARRY!* NO DOUBT HE'S TRYING TO MAKE UP TO ME--BUT I WON'T GIVE HIM A TUMBLE!

HOWEVER, AS IRIS ROUNDS THE CORNER...

GOOD GOSH! THAT COULDN'T HAVE BEEN BARRY ALLEN I JUST SAW-- BECAUSE THERE HE IS SITTING IN THAT BUS!

AS THE DAY WEARS ON...

THIS IS *UNCANNY!* WHEREVER I GO I SEEM TO SEE *BARRY ALLEN!* THERE HE IS AGAIN--AS A *STORE MODEL!*

FINALLY, THAT EVENING...

I--I TRIED TO DRIVE YOU FROM MY MIND, BARRY... BUT I GUESS I COULDN'T! WHEREVER I WENT TODAY I SEEMED TO SEE YOUR IMAGE...

MY PLAN WORKED!

I USED THE MIRROR-MASTER'S IMAGE-PROJECTOR TO SEND IMAGES OF MYSELF ACROSS THE CITY TO HAUNT IRIS--AND SHE THOUGHT IT WAS JUST A TRICK OF HER MIND--AS I HOPED SHE WOULD!

NO SENSE TRYING TO FIGHT THIS, IRIS-- IT'S...ER... BIGGER THAN BOTH OF US!

TENDERLY, THE PAIR MAKE A DATE...

ALL RIGHT...BUT REMEMBER, BARRY-- DON'T BE LATE!

DON'T WORRY, IRIS! WILD HORSES COULDN'T KEEP ME FROM MEETING YOU ON TIME!

BUT WHEN THE EAGER YOUNG MAN HURRIES TO GET READY...

WHOO! SLIPPED-- ON ONE OF THE MIRROR-MASTER'S SHINY MIRRORS THAT FELL TO THE FLOOR--!

AND SO POOR BARRY IS TEMPORARILY KAYOED...

...TO AWAKEN A HALF HOUR LATER WITH A BUMP ON HIS ACHING NOGGIN!

MEANWHILE...

THIRTY MINUTES LATE! THIS IS THE END! I WILL NEVER MAKE A DATE WITH BARRY ALLEN AGAIN-- NEVER!

The End.

13

IN THE PRESS ALL OVER THE COUNTRY...

DAILY PLANET 5¢

FRED JANSEN IN ORBIT!

The SPACE NEWS 10¢

ASTRONAUT CIRCLING EARTH 1000 MILES IN SPACE!

DAILY EVENING STAR 1¢¢

MAN-CARRYING SATELLITE TO ORBIT FOR 50 HOURS!

BUT 30 HOURS LATER, THE "HUMAN" SATELLITE UNACCOUNTABLY PLUMMETS EARTHWARD...

GUIDING MECHANISM JAMMED... PLUNGING INTO WATER...

AS THE SATELLITE CONTINUES ITS DOWNWARD PLUNGE...

HAVEN'T HIT BOTTOM YET! I MUST BE SINKING INTO AN OCEAN!

DAYS LATER...

STILL NO WORD ABOUT FRED JANSEN! SINCE HE HAD AIR FOR ONLY THREE DAYS IN THE SATELLITE -- AND IT IS NOW TEN DAYS SINCE HE VANISHED -- HE MUST BE PRESUMED DEAD...

ON THE AIR

BUT AT THAT MOMENT ON ONE OF THE NAVY VESSELS GRAPPLING FOR THE SUNKEN SATELLITE...

WE'VE HOOKED ONTO SOMETHING!

BRING IT UP!

SOON...

OF COURSE POOR JANSEN CAN'T BE ALIVE -- BUT AT LEAST WE'VE RECOVERED THE SATELLITE FOR SCIENTIFIC EXAMINATION!

IT'S THE SATELLITE!

2

BUT INCREDIBLY, WHEN THE SATELLITE IS OPENED...

JANSEN--ALIVE?!

HI... CAPTAIN! GET ME OUT OF THIS SARDINE CAN... WILL YOU?

AS NAVY DOCTORS ARE QUICKLY RUSHED TO THE RESCUED MAN...

AMAZING! BY ALL ORDINARY LAWS HE SHOULD HAVE PERISHED!

HE HARDLY SHOWS ANY ILL EFFECTS!

ON A NATION-WIDE HOOKUP LATER...

PEOPLE KEEP ASKING HOW IT FEELS TO BE BURIED UNDER THE SEA SO LONG! BUT I CAN'T TELL -- I MUST HAVE BEEN UNCONSCIOUS ALMOST ALL THE TIME!

AFTER THE FUROR HAS DIED DOWN, FRED JANSEN HAS DINNER WITH AN OLD FRIEND...

I DIDN'T WANT TO MENTION THIS ON TELEVISION, BARRY! I FIGURED PEOPLE WOULD LAUGH! BUT -- SINCE I WAS PULLED UP FROM THE BOTTOM OF THE OCEAN I'VE HAD STRANGE DREAMS...

AS THE FLYER'S COMPANION, POLICE SCIENTIST BARRY ALLEN, EXPRESSES SURPRISE.

STRANGE -- IN WHAT WAY, FRED?

FOR ONE THING, IT'S ALWAYS THE SAME DREAM! I KEEP DREAMING ABOUT WHAT HAPPENED TO ME ON THE BOTTOM OF THE SEA!

"LISTEN, BARRY! THE DREAM ALWAYS STARTS WITH ME IN THE SATELLITE... PLUNGING DOWN... DOWN BENEATH THE SURFACE..."

THE IMPACT... THE STRAIN! LOSING CONSCIOUSNESS..!

3

"AND WHEN I COME TO, AMAZINGLY..."

W-WHERE AM I?

DO NOT FEAR! *YOU* ARE IN OUR *SEA-CITY* OF *SAREME!* YOU LANDED NEAR US... WE RESCUED YOU!

"AS I CALM DOWN... AND LEARN ABOUT THE UNSUSPECTED UNDERSEA WORLD..."

IN SOME INCREDIBLE WAY WE ARE ABLE TO COMMUNICATE BY *TELEPATHY!*

WE HERE IN *SAREME* HAVE LONG BELIEVED THAT THERE WAS LIFE ABOVE US... ABOVE THE SEA...

...AND WE WANTED TO SEE IT! BUT MANY OF OUR PEOPLE LOST THEIR LIVES TRYING TO REACH THE SURFACE! THAT'S WHY-- *YOU* ARE SO IMPORTANT TO US!

I DON'T UNDER-STAND...!

"SUDDENLY THE *LEADER* OF THE GROUP COMES CLOSE TO ME..."

WE IN *SAREME* ARE IN DANGER! OUR ENEMIES THE *MAUGITES* ARE OUT TO DESTROY US! YOU MUST HELP US... SOMEHOW!

I? BUT--?

THIS IS OUR PLAN! WE WILL SEND YOU BACK TO YOUR WORLD! CLEARLY IT IS A WORLD OF MUCH SCIENCE AND GREAT POWER! WHEN YOU ARE THERE DO NOT FORGET US! FIND A WAY TO HELP US-- QUICKLY!

4

THE REST OF THE DREAM IS KIND OF MIXED UP, BARRY! I KNOW THAT THEY PUT ME BACK IN THE CAPSULE... AND THEN...

"...SOMEHOW THEY GET IT OUT INTO THE WATER AGAIN..."

I'VE LEARNED THAT THE SAREMITES CAN STAY FOR A FEW HOURS UNDERWATER, BUT THEN THEY HAVE TO RETURN TO THEIR SEA-CITY...

ACCORDING TO WHAT THEY TOLD ME, THE AIR IN THEIR SEA-CITY IS MAINTAINED BY RIVERS OF AIR THAT COME DOWN THROUGH THE EARTH... THROUGH THE ROOF OF THEIR CAVERN!

AND THE SEA IS KEPT BACK FROM THE CAVERN BY THE AIR PRESSURE INSIDE THERE! BUT-- WHAT'S THIS? A NAVY GRAPPLING HOOK!?

"I KNEW THEN WHAT THE SAREMITES MEANT BY SAYING THEY HAD A PLAN TO GET ME BACK ON THE SURFACE!"

THEY MUST HAVE SEEN THIS HOOK MOVING AROUND HERE-- AND FIGURED SOMEONE ABOVE WAS TRYING TO FIND ME AND THE SATELLITE! NOW THEY'RE ATTACHING THE HOOK--!

"SOON..."

I'M BEING DRAWN UP! I'M RETURNING TO THE SURFACE!

5

YOU KNOW THE REST, BARRY! ACTUALLY THE DREAM SEEMS TO **END** AS I REACH THE SURFACE...

MENU

As THE TWO FRIENDS PART...

OF COURSE IT'S JUST A DREAM, BARRY! BUT -- IT SEEMS SO VIVID -- I JUST HAD TO TELL YOU ABOUT IT!

I'M GLAD YOU DID, FRED...

RESTAURANT

LATER, AS **BARRY ALLEN** HEADS HOMEWARD ALONE...

STRANGE! THAT DREAM OF FRED'S COULD EXPLAIN ONE MYSTERY -- **HOW** HE WAS ABLE TO REMAIN ALIVE UNDER THE SEA FOR **TEN DAYS!**

DANCE

EAT

AND THE MORE I THINK ABOUT IT, THE MORE IT SEEMS TO ME THAT THE DREAM MAY **NOT** HAVE BEEN A DREAM AT ALL! IT COULD HAVE **ACTUALLY HAPPENED** --

-- AND MADE SUCH AN IMPRESSION ON FRED JANSEN'S MIND THAT HE'S BEEN **DREAM-ING ABOUT IT EVER SINCE!** BY MERCURY! I'LL BET THAT'S IT!

BUS STOP

THE **SEA-CITY OF SAREME** ACTUALLY EXISTS ON THE BOTTOM OF THE OCEAN! BUT I DON'T HAVE TO WONDER ABOUT IT --

ON A SHADOWY CORNER OF TOWN, A BRIGHT SPURT OF RED SHOOTS FROM A RING ON BARRY ALLEN'S FINGER...

AS *THE FLASH*--MY SECRET ALTER EGO--I CAN FIND OUT--QUICKER THAN A FISH CAN SHAKE ITS TAIL!

JUST AS A NAVY SEA-RAFT EXPANDS ON CONTACT WITH WATER, SO THE TINY UNIFORM IN THE RING EXPANDS IN CONTACT WITH AIR...

AND INSTANTS LATER A STREAKING CRIMSON FIGURE IS DIVING INTO THE SEA...

THE CHEMICAL EXPLOSION WHICH ACCIDENTALLY GAVE MY BODY ITS TERRIFIC SPEED--

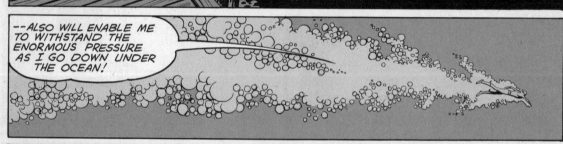

--ALSO WILL ENABLE ME TO WITHSTAND THE ENORMOUS PRESSURE AS I GO DOWN UNDER THE OCEAN!

DOWN, DOWN GOES THE *WORLD'S FASTEST HUMAN*...

ACCORDING TO FRED'S DREAM, THE *SAREMITES* ARE IN PERIL! IF THEY REALLY EXIST, *I MUST* TRY TO HELP THEM!

FOLLOWING FRED JANSEN'S DESCRIPTION OF THE STRANGE CAVERN'S LOCATION, THE *SCARLET SPEEDSTER* QUICKLY FINDS...

THE *OPENING* FRED DESCRIBED--WITH THE SEA HELD BACK BY *AIR PRESSURE* INSIDE!

7

THEN, A SPLIT-MOMENT LATER...

FRED'S "DREAM WORLD" OF SAREME IS REAL!

AS FLASH CONFRONTS THE SAREMITES...

I AM A FRIEND OF THE HUMAN FROM THE SURFACE WHOSE LIFE YOU SAVED--

WE KNOW, FLASH...

WE OF SAREME ARE A VERY PRIMITIVE RACE-- ACCORDING TO YOUR STANDARDS! BUT SOMEHOW WE HAVE THE ABILITY OF TELEPATHY! BY READING YOUR MIND, WE HAVE LEARNED OF YOUR AMAZING POWERS...

...AND WE BELIEVE YOU ARE THE ONLY ONE WHO CAN HELP US! LISTEN, OUR ENEMIES THE MAUGITES ARE VICIOUS--

-- AND IT IS BECAUSE OF THEIR SPEED THAT WE CAN HARDLY DEFEND OURSELVES AGAINST THEM!

WHO ARE THESE MAUGITES? WHERE DO THEY COME FROM?

8

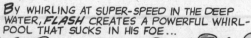
By whirling at super-speed in the deep water, *FLASH* creates a powerful whirlpool that sucks in his foe...

THE WHIRLPOOL I'VE MADE IS PULLING IN THE *MAUGITES*-- SPINNING THEM AROUND HELPLESSLY! I'VE DEFEATED THEM IN THEIR OWN ELEMENT!

FLEEING! AND THIS TIME THEY'RE *NOT* TURNING AROUND!

As the *KING OF SUPER-SPEED* makes the cavern again with the last reserves of air in his lungs...

WHEW! FEELS GOOD TO *BREATHE* AGAIN!

WELL, MAYBE I'VE SHOWN YOU NOW THAT THE *MAUGITES* CAN BE BEATEN--

YES! WHAT YOU HAVE BEGUN-- WE SHALL FINISH! WE WILL FIND A WAY-- SOMEHOW-- TO SURVIVE!

As the *FLASH* takes a last look around him...

GOOD! IT'S BETTER FOR THE *SAREMITES* TO TRIUMPH OVER THEIR ENEMY BY THEIR OWN EFFORTS! IT'S THE ONLY WAY THEY CAN KEEP THEIR *SELF-RESPECT!* EH? WHAT'S *THAT*--?

IT'S A WEAPON I THOUGHT OF... TO USE AGAINST THE *MAUGITES!*

A PRIMITIVE *BOW AND ARROW!*

NOW I'M SURE THE *SAREMITES* WILL BE ABLE TO DEFEND THEIR *SEA-CITY!* THEY'VE BEGUN TO INVENT WEAPONS--JUST AS OUR RACE DID ON THE SURFACE THOUSANDS OF YEARS AGO WHEN WE WERE CAVEMEN--AND FOUGHT OTHER ANIMALS FOR SURVIVAL!

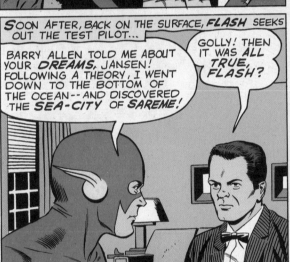

Soon AFTER, BACK ON THE SURFACE, *FLASH* SEEKS OUT THE TEST PILOT...

BARRY ALLEN TOLD ME ABOUT YOUR *DREAMS*, JANSEN! FOLLOWING A THEORY, I WENT DOWN TO THE BOTTOM OF THE OCEAN--AND DISCOVERED THE *SEA-CITY* OF *SAREME!*

GOLLY! THEN IT WAS *ALL TRUE, FLASH?*

YES! BUT TURN OUT THE LIGHT FOR A MOMENT, WILL YOU?

EH? OF COURSE--

The NEXT MOMENT...

YOU REMEMBER THE STRANGE *YELLOW STONES* THAT GAVE OFF LIGHT IN THE CAVERN BELOW? THEY ARE THE ONLY SOURCES OF LIGHT THE *SAREMITES* HAVE...

IN GRATITUDE FOR YOUR BRING-ING THEIR APPEAL FOR HELP TO THE SURFACE THEY HAD THIS RING MADE--AND ASKED ME TO GIVE IT TO YOU!

I'LL *ALWAYS* TREASURE IT!

The End

12

IN THE CENTRAL CITY POLICE LABORATORY WHERE BARRY ALLEN [ALIAS THE FLASH] WORKS AS A RESEARCH SCIENTIST...

I MUSTN'T FORGET... I'VE GOT A DATE WITH IRIS IN EXACTLY ONE HOUR! AND I'D BETTER BE ON TIME--ESPECIALLY AFTER WHAT HAPPENED THE LAST TIME I WAS LATE!

IRIS WAS SO MAD, SHE REFUSED EVER TO SEE ME AGAIN! BUT I GOT HER TO AGREE SHE'D FORGIVE ME IF I MET HER A DOZEN TIMES IN A ROW ON TIME! SO FAR, I'VE BEEN PUNCTUAL ON ELEVEN DATES-- AND THE BIG TWELFTH ONE COMES UP TODAY!

AS A MATTER OF FACT I BETTER START FOR OUR DATE NOW-- JUST TO BE SAFE! I'VE FINISHED MY WORK HERE FOR THIS AFTERNOON!

BUT THEN SUDDENLY OVER THE POLICE INTERCOM...

... AND A CLOUDBURST HAS JUST STRUCK DOWNTOWN, ENDANGERING PEOPLE!

CLOUD-BURST--!?

ON A SUNNY DAY LIKE THIS ONE? THIS SOUNDS LIKE SOMETHING THE FLASH BETTER HAVE A LOOK AT!

OUT OF BARRY'S RING SHOOTS A TINY RED SUIT THAT GROWS LARGER... LARGER... ON CONTACT WITH THE AIR...

...LIKE A NAVY LIFE RAFT WHEN IT HITS THE SEA...

2

AND SPLINTER-SECONDS LATER, ON THE STREETS OF CENTRAL CITY, A BRILLIANT SCARLET SHAPE APPEARS...

THE FLASH!

DOWN ON MAIN STREET THE ANNOUNCEMENT SAID! BUT I DON'T SEE...

AROUND A CORNER...

GREAT SCOTT! IT IS POURING HERE! BUT-- WHAT'S THAT!?

IT'S ABOUT TIME THE FOLKS OF THIS TOWN MET THE WEATHER WIZARD! HA HA ...

ON A HOT DAY LIKE THIS A LITTLE RAIN FEELS GOOD! AND WHEN I FEEL LIKE A LITTLE RAIN-- I MAKE IT RAIN!

THEN AS THE SUSPICIOUS SPEEDSTER WHIRLS AT THE BIZARRE FIGURE...

FLASH--TRYING TO STOP MY LITTLE SPORT? I'LL PROVE YOU CAN'T, MY "FLASHY" FRIEND--

A BOLT OF LIGHTNING--SHOOTING OUT OF THAT STICK OF HIS-- STRAIGHT AT ME--!

3.

INSTANTLY THE *FASTEST MAN ALIVE* BURSTS INTO ACTION...

I'VE OFTEN BEEN CALLED "FAST AS LIGHTNING"-- BUT THIS IS THE FIRST CHANCE I'VE HAD TO PROVE I'M EVEN *FASTER!*

YOU--YOU *DODGED* MY LIGHTNING BOLT?

THAT'S NOT ALL I'M GOING TO DO --

IN A WHIRL OF *SUPER-SPEED* THE MIGHTY *FLASH* CIRCLES HIS FOE...

BY SPINNING AROUND HIM THIS WAY I'VE CREATED A NEAR-*VACUUM* IN THE CENTER OF THIS CIRCLE! HE WON'T HAVE ENOUGH AIR TO BREATHE! IT WILL WEAKEN HIM SO I CAN GRAB HIM!

BUT AS THE SELF-STYLED *WEATHER WIZARD* BEGINS TO GASP FOR BREATH...

GOT TO ACT FAST... CAN'T--CAN'T LET THE *FLASH*-- DEFEAT ME THIS WAY--!

AND OUT OF THE AMAZING *WEATHER-STICK* POURS A THICK SMOKE-LIKE FOG...

CAN'T SEE A THING-- IT'S BLINDING ME!

4

"KEEPING OUT OF SIGHT, THE FUGITIVE HEADED FOR THE LAKE REGION..."

I'VE GOT A QUEER-DUCK BROTHER NAMED CLYDE WHO LIVES ALL BY HIMSELF LIKE A HERMIT ON *BIG WATER LAKE!* HE SEEMED TO TRY TO GET AWAY FROM THE WORLD...

...AS IF HE DIDN'T LIKE PEOPLE! BUT WHETHER HE LIKES IT OR NOT, BROTHER CLYDE *IS* GOING TO GET A *VISITOR!*

"MARDON DIDN'T KNOW TOO MUCH ABOUT HIS BROTHER! HE WAS PRETTY SURPRISED WHEN FINALLY HE REACHED THE LITTLE ISLAND..."

≶ WHEW! ≶ WHAT KIND OF A LAY-OUT HAS CLYDE GOT HERE? LOOKS LIKE... A... *SCIENTIFIC LABORATORY*--

BUT WHERE'S CLYDE? SO FAR I HAVEN'T COME ACROSS A SIGN OF LIFE ON THIS CLAM SHELL!

"THEN SUDDENLY THE ESCAPED CONVICT FOUND HIS BROTHER..."

...*DEAD!* HE--HE MUST HAVE HAD A HEART ATTACK OR SOMETHING HERE WHILE HE WAS WORKING! BUT-- WHAT'S THIS?

"FROM NEAR HIS BROTHER'S HAND MARDON TOOK THE NOTEBOOK THAT WAS TO PROVE HIS MOST VALUABLE FIND!"

EH? ALL ABOUT HIS *EXPERIMENTS* IN *CONTROLLING THE WEATHER!* IS THIS WHAT CLYDE WAS DOING HERE ALL THESE YEARS?

6

"MARDON STUDIED THE NOTES WHILE HE WAS HIDING OUT! HIS CUNNING MIND SAW SOMETHING..."

CLYDE WAS A FOOL! HE ONLY EXPERIMENTED IN ORDER TO HELP PEOPLE--AND HE WAS ABOUT TO ANNOUNCE HIS DISCOVERIES TO THE WORLD WHEN HE DIED! BUT I HAVE A BETTER IDEA...

THESE DISCOVERIES OF CLYDE'S CAN MAKE ME RICH--AND POWERFUL! BUT EVEN MORE IMPORTANT, THEY CAN MAKE IT POSSIBLE FOR ME TO CARRY OUT A PRIVATE PROJECT I'VE BEEN THINKING ABOUT!

"THE WILY CONVICT IMMEDIATELY SET TO WORK..."

I'VE BUILT THIS ELECTRO-VIBRATOR WAND--MY WEATHER-STICK--ALONG THE PRINCIPLES THAT CLYDE DISCOVERED! IT WILL ENABLE ME TO HAVE COMPLETE CONTROL OVER THE ATMOSPHERE--TO CREATE ALL KINDS OF WEATHER EFFECTS--

--AND SOME THAT NO WEATHER-MAN EVER HEARD OF! BUT NOW TO GO WITH MY NEW ROLE AS THE WEATHER WIZARD I NEED THE PROPER COSTUME--SOMETHING BIZARRE AND ORIGINAL!

"IT DID NOT TAKE MARDON LONG TO WORK OUT A SUITABLE COSTUME..."

AH! IT'S PERFECT!

7

ALL THAT I'VE TOLD YOU, *FLASH*, WE PIECED TOGETHER AFTER TRACING MARDON'S MOVEMENTS FROM THE TIME HE ESCAPED FROM THE DEPUTY GUARD! AFTER HE LEFT THE ISLAND...

"MARDON--THE *WEATHER WIZARD*--LOST NO TIME IN PUTTING HIS NEW POWERS TO USE..."

WHAT'S THIS? *COLORED SNOW* FALLING HERE *INSIDE THE BANK!?*

HA HA! I'VE PUT ON QUITE A SHOW HERE --

-- SO IT'S ONLY FAIR THAT I PAY MYSELF A *NICE FAT FEE*-- WHILE THE TELLERS ARE TOO POP-EYED WITH ASTONISHMENT TO EVEN NOTICE ME!

"HE KEPT EXPERIMENTING WITH HIS AMAZING *WEATHER-STICK* OUT OF A SENSE OF BRAVADO AND CONTEMPT FOR PEOPLE..."

LOOK AT THE YOKELS STARE -- AT THIS *RAIN-BOW* I'VE CREATED RIGHT HERE ON THE STREET!

"*IT* WAS THEN THAT MARDON BEGAN ON HIS *PET PROJECT!* WE FOUND OUT ABOUT THIS FROM NOTES HE INADVERTENTLY LEFT BEHIND ON THE ISLAND..."

HAILSTONES-- THE SIZE OF CANNON-BALLS--DESTROYING THAT *POLICE STATION!*

8

AFTER THAT, *FLASH*, HE ATTACKED THE SHERIFF'S OFFICE IN A NEARBY STATE! WE HAVEN'T BEEN ABLE TO FIGURE OUT...

THAT'S AN IMPORTANT CLUE, MARSHAL! WAIT...

AFTER A MOMENT'S THOUGHT ON THE PART OF THE FAMED SPEEDSTER...

IT MAY TELL ME WHERE THAT SELF-STYLED *WEATHER-WIZARD* WILL STRIKE NEXT! BUT I'VE NO TIME TO EXPLAIN! SEE YOU LATER--

IF I'M RIGHT I'VE GOT TO GET TO A CERTAIN *HOUSE* IN THE SUBURBS OF *CENTRAL CITY* AT ONCE! MARDON MAY BE ATTACKING THERE AT THIS MOMENT!

AND SCARCELY A *FLASH*-SECOND LATER IN THE SUBURBS...

GREAT SCOTT! I WAS RIGHT! THE *WIZARD* HAS CREATED A HUGE GLACIER -- THREATENING THAT ISOLATED HOUSE...

-- EVEN CENTRAL CITY ITSELF MAY BE DOOMED!

YOU CAN'T STOP IT, *FLASH!* NO ONE CAN INTERFERE WITH ONE OF MY *PROJECTS!*

9

I'LL HANDLE MARDON LATER! RIGHT NOW I'VE GOT TO STOP THAT GLACIER -- ONE OF THE MOST TERRIBLE FORCES IN NATURE! BUT HOW--?

AS FLASH CONCEIVES OF A PLAN...

I NOTICED THESE MEN USING AN ACETYLENE TORCH AS I CAME BY AN INSTANT AGO! THEY WON'T MIND MY BORROWING IT IN AN EMERGENCY LIKE THIS!

THEN, LIGHTING THE TORCH, THE FASTEST MAN ALIVE BEGINS TO RACE BACK AND FORTH ALONG THE FRONT OF THE GLACIER...

THIS ACETYLENE TORCH HAS ONE OF THE HOTTEST FLAMES KNOWN! AND BY APPLYING IT TO THE GLACIER THIS WAY I'VE GOT PRACTICALLY THE ENTIRE GLACIER FRONT MELTING!

BUT THEN...

HA HA! YOU STOPPED MY GLACIER, FLASH -- BUT IN MELTING IT YOU CAUSED A FLASH FLOOD THAT WILL DO EVEN MORE DAMAGE!

HE'S RIGHT!

LIKE A WINK THE SCARLET SPEEDSTER IS AGAIN ON HIS WAY...

GOT TO HEAD OFF THAT WAVE OF WATER AND STOP IT BEFORE IT HITS THE CITY! AND ONLY A MOMENT OR TWO TO DO IT--

10

OUTSTRIPPING THE RUSHING FLOOD BY A MIGHTY BURST OF SUPER-SPEED, FLASH GETS IN FRONT OF IT AND...

GREAT CYCLONES! THE FLASH IS WHIRLING HIS ARMS AROUND SO FAST THAT HE'S CREATED A HUGE WIND -- DRIVING BACK THE WATERS AND DISPERSING THEM HARMLESSLY!

I'LL GET RID OF FLASH NOW -- ONCE AND FOR ALL! HE'LL LEARN THAT IT DOESN'T PAY TO INTERFERE WITH THE WEATHER WIZARD!

AS THE MASTER OF THE ATMOSPHERE POINTS HIS WEATHER-STICK UPWARD, AN OVERHANGING CLOUD ABOVE GATHERS ITSELF TOGETHER AND...

HE'S PULLING THE CLOUD DOWN TOWARD HIM! INCREDIBLE!

THE FOLLOWING MOMENT...

THE DUST AND SOOT PARTICLES IN THE CLOUD -- SOLIDIFIED INTO A HARD MASS BY MY WEATHER-STICK -- WILL BLAST FLASH APART WHEN IT HITS HIM!

BUT AS THE THREATENING CLOUD-POINT DRIVES AT THE WORLD'S FASTEST HUMAN...

WHEW! ONLY MY SPEED SAVED ME!

11

WITH A TREMENDOUS SURGE OF SPEED, *FLASH* SLAMS TOWARD HIS FOE...

...AT SUCH A RATE THAT THE AIR IN FRONT OF HIM PILES UP INTO A *WAVE-FRONT*...

...AND A SPLIT-INSTANT LATER STRIKES MARDON LIKE A SOLID SHEET OF *GLASS*...

AS THE *SCARLET SPEEDSTER* SHOULDERS HIS KAYOED OPPONENT...

I GUESS I SHOWED THE *WEATHER WIZARD* A FEW TRICKS WITH THE ATMOSPHERE THAT EVEN HE DIDN'T KNOW ABOUT! NOW TO GET HIM TO THE POLICE!

AND SOON AFTER, WITH THE *WIZARD* BEHIND BARS...

YOU SEE, MR. MARSHAL, WHEN YOU TOLD ME THAT MARDON HAD ATTACKED A *POLICE STATION* IN ONE TOWN AND A *SHERIFF'S OFFICE* IN ANOTHER, IT GAVE ME AN IDEA...

I REMEMBERED THEN THAT I'D HEARD OF MARK MARDON TOO! AND THAT HE'D ONCE BEEN ARRESTED FOR BURGLARY IN *CENTRAL CITY*! I EVEN RECALLED THAT THE MAN WHO ARRESTED HIM WAS A POLICE LIEUTENANT NAMED *JIM HARVEY*...

THE NOTION CAME TO ME THAT MARDON'S *PET PROJECT* WAS TO TAKE REVENGE ON THE THREE POLICE OFFICERS WHO HAD ARRESTED HIM IN HIS CRIMINAL CAREER! AND IT TURNED OUT I WAS RIGHT!

12

The FLASH
MEET KID FLASH!

BARRY ALLEN, ALIAS THE **FLASH**, THOUGHT THAT HE ALONE IN ALL THE WORLD POSSESSED THE **GIFT OF SUPER-SPEED!** AND BARRY'S BELIEF WAS CORRECT--UNTIL ONE MOMENTOUS DAY WHEN AN INCREDIBLE ACCIDENT HAPPENED -- AN ACCIDENT THAT RESULTED IN THE APPEARANCE OF A **STARTLING NEW FIGURE** IN THE CONTINUOUS COMBAT AGAINST EVIL AND INJUSTICE!

I RUSHED HERE TO THE ZOO TO HELP GET THOSE ESCAPED BEASTS BACK INTO THEIR CAGES-- BUT FAST AS *I* WAS--*KID FLASH* BEAT ME TO IT!!

NOON TIME...IN THE APARTMENT OF **BARRY ALLEN**...

IRIS ASKED TO SEE ME HERE! SHE SAID SHE WAS BRINGING OVER SOMEONE TO MEET ME! I WONDER WHO IT COULD BE...

WITHIN A FEW MOMENTS...

BARRY, I WANT YOU TO MEET MY NEPHEW WALLY! HE'S THE PRESIDENT OF THE **FLASH FAN CLUB** IN HIS HOME TOWN!

HMM! HI, WALLY...

WALLY'S AMBITION IS TO MEET HIS HERO, THE **FLASH!** I THOUGHT YOU MIGHT BE ABLE TO HELP ARRANGE IT, BARRY...

I SEE!

IRIS KNOWS I'M A FRIEND OF **FLASH**--

--BUT SHE **DOESN'T** KNOW WE'RE ONE AND THE SAME PERSON! NOW-- HOW CAN I DO WHAT SHE ASKS-- AND INTRODUCE **FLASH** TO HER NEPHEW **WITHOUT** REVEALING THAT FACT? WAIT--I HAVE AN IDEA...

AS BARRY TURNS TO THE BOY'S PRETTY AUNT...

IRIS, SUPPOSE YOU LEAVE WALLY WITH ME FOR THE AFTERNOON? MAYBE I CAN ARRANGE A MEETING WITH **FLASH!**

OKAY--I'VE GOT TO GET BACK TO MY DESK AT **PICTURE NEWS** ANYWAY! SEE YOU TWO LATER...

AFTER IRIS HAS GONE...

JUMPING JETS! YOU MEAN I'M REALLY GOING TO MEET **THE FLASH**, MR. ALLEN?

I THINK SO, WALLY...

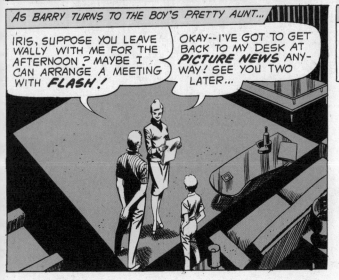

2

As WALLY DOES ENTER...

I MOVED SO FAST, HE DIDN'T EVEN SEE THE DOOR OPENING AND CLOSING BEFORE HE REACHED IT! --HERE HE COMES!

JUMPING JETS!

FLASH!? IS IT REALLY YOU?

HI, WALLY! I COULDN'T--ER-- HELP OVERHEAR-ING THE CONVER-SATION IN THE NEXT ROOM! AND I'M GLAD MY FRIEND, BARRY ALLEN, SENT YOU IN TO SEE ME!

IT ISN'T OFTEN I GET A CHANCE TO MEET THE PRESIDENT OF ONE OF MY FAN CLUBS!

MR. FLASH, THIS IS THE COOLEST MOMENT OF MY LIFE!

I MEAN--WAIT TILL THE CATS BACK HOME HEAR I'VE ACTUALLY SHAKEN HANDS WITH THE FLASH HIMSELF!

THE CATS?

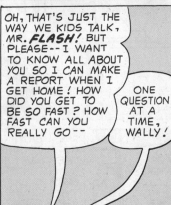

OH, THAT'S JUST THE WAY WE KIDS TALK, MR. FLASH! BUT PLEASE--I WANT TO KNOW ALL ABOUT YOU SO I CAN MAKE A REPORT WHEN I GET HOME! HOW DID YOU GET TO BE SO FAST? HOW FAST CAN YOU REALLY GO--

ONE QUESTION AT A TIME, WALLY!

BUT I'LL DO BETTER THAN JUST ANSWER YOUR FIRST QUESTION! I'LL ACTUALLY SHOW YOU HOW I GOT MY SPEED! WOULD YOU LIKE THAT?

MAN!-- WOULD I!?

I'VE TAKEN WALLY TO THIS LITTLE PRIVATE LABORATORY IN BARRY ALLEN'S APARTMENT--AND EXPLAINED TO HIM THAT BARRY HIMSELF HAD TO LEAVE FOR A WHILE!

IT WAS TWO YEARS AGO, WALLY...

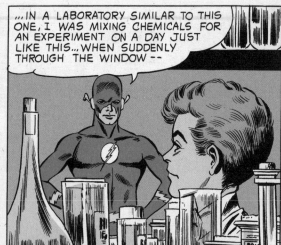

...IN A LABORATORY SIMILAR TO THIS ONE, I WAS MIXING CHEMICALS FOR AN EXPERIMENT ON A DAY JUST LIKE THIS...WHEN SUDDENLY THROUGH THE WINDOW --

-- A LIGHTNING BOLT--HUH ??

GREAT SCOTT! JUST AS I WAS TELLING WALLY ABOUT THE LIGHTNING BOLT--A REAL ONE CAME THROUGH THE WINDOW!

WALLY, ARE YOU ALL RIGHT?

I--I THINK SO...

THE LIGHTNING HIT THE BOTTLES AND SPLASHED THE CHEMICALS OVER WALLY IN THE SAME WAY IT DID OVER ME TWO YEARS AGO... GREAT JUPITER--? I WONDER --

5

IT SEEMS FANTASTIC! BUT-- THE ACCIDENT WAS EXACTLY THE SAME! CAN IT BE--IS IT POSSIBLE--THAT *WALLY* NOW HAS THE *SPEED OF FLASH?*

THERE'S A QUICK WAY TO FIND OUT! IF HE'S GOT THE SPEED IT WILL SHOW IMMEDIATELY...

WALLY... BEFORE WE GO ON, WILL YOU DO ME A FAVOR?

I'D LIKE TO SEE HOW FAST YOU CAN RUN! WILL YOU TRY--JUST TRY TO RACE ME TO THE END OF THE APARTMENT THERE--AND BACK--A FEW TIMES?

RACE *YOU?*

AS YOUNG WALLY GIVES HIS AMAZED CONSENT...

LET'S GO!

HE'S RIGHT WITH ME! BUT I'M NOT GOING MY FASTEST! NOW I'LL REALLY START TO MOVE--

I--I'M GOING AT SUPER-SPEED--AND HE'S RIGHT ALONGSIDE ME!!

I GUESS *FLASH* ISN'T HALF TRYING BECAUSE...I'M KEEPING UP WITH HIM!

6

AS THE BOY DOES AS BIDDEN AND A SPURT OF RED PUFFS SUDDENLY FROM THE RING...

IT'S A UNIFORM-- JUST LIKE YOURS!

YES! IT'S ONE OF MY SPARES--BUT I'VE CUT IT DOWN TO FIT YOU! TRY IT ON!

IN NO TIME AT ALL...

IT FITS YOU FINE! NO ONE WILL RECOGNIZE YOU WHEN YOU WEAR THIS OUTFIT, WALLY--AND YOU MUST KEEP YOUR IDENTITY A SECRET--TO SAFEGUARD YOUR PRECIOUS GIFT OF SUPER-SPEED! BUT WE'VE STILL GOT TO FIND A NAME FOR YOU...

IN A FLASH--THE FLASH COMES UP WITH AN APT TITLE FOR THE JUVENILE SPEEDSTER...

YOU TALKED ABOUT THE KIDS BACK HOME, WALLY--SUPPOSE WE CALL YOU KID FLASH-- THE FASTEST BOY ALIVE! HOW DOES THAT STRIKE YOU?

KID FLASH!? THAT'S OUT OF THIS WORLD-- WAY OUT!

THEN, AS THE FASTEST MAN ALIVE NOTICES THE TIME...

BARRY ALLEN HAS TO GET BACK TO WORK!

WALLY, I'VE GOT TO LEAVE FOR AWHILE! YOU CAN STAY HERE--AND PRACTICE YOUR SPEED TILL YOU MASTER IT!

I'LL BE BACK BEFORE DARK!

OKAY, MR. FLASH! SEE YOU--!

WHEN WALLY IS LEFT ALONE...

WHEN I TELL THE CATS BACK HOME--BUT WAIT! I WON'T BE ABLE TO TELL THEM! I MUST REMEMBER WHAT MR. FLASH SAID...

8

I CAN'T REVEAL TO **ANYONE** WHO I REALLY AM! AND ONLY MR. **FLASH** WILL KNOW MY TRUE IDENTITY! GOLLY, THIS IS THE MOST EXCITING THING THAT EVER HAPPENED TO ANYBODY!

BUT THEN, OVER THE RADIO IN THE APARTMENT...

...AND SEVERAL **DANGEROUS ANIMALS** ESCAPED FROM THE **ZOO**! THE PUBLIC IS WARNED--

ANIMALS ESCAPED? JUMPING JETS!

AS **KID FLASH** GETS AN IDEA...

MR. **FLASH** TOLD ME TO PRACTICE MY SPEED--AND HE ALSO SAID I MUST HELP ANYONE IN DANGER! HERE'S MY CHANCE TO DO **BOTH**!

I'LL GET RIGHT OVER TO THE **ZOO**--AND HELP OUT! MAYBE I CAN PREVENT THOSE **DANGEROUS ANIMALS** FROM HURTING ANYONE!

LIKE A TINY STREAK OF SCARLET, THE **FASTEST BOY ALIVE** SCOOTS ACROSS THE CITY...

JEEPERS-WEEPERS! I'M GOING PAST THAT SPEEDING **SPORT CAR** AS IF IT WERE IN REVERSE!! THIS **SUPER-SPEED** IS THE COOLEST-- THE **MOST**!

9

AT A STREET CORNER, A SIGHT ARRESTS THE PINT-SIZED **SPEEDSTER**...

THAT OLD MAN--HE'S HAVING TROUBLE GETTING ACROSS THE STREET WITH ALL THIS TRAFFIC!

SPLIT-SECONDS AFTER...

A SUDDEN GUST OF WIND BLEW ME ACROSS THE STREET!

BOY, THE THINGS YOU CAN DO WITH **SUPER-SPEED**-- HELP PEOPLE--MOVE AROUND LIKE LIGHTNING!

AT THE ZOO, TWO SHAKES LATER...

I HEARD THE HEAD-KEEPER SAY THAT A FIRED EMPLOYEE LET A LION AND A BEAR ESCAPE FROM THEIR CAGES ON PURPOSE! THE EMPLOYEE HAS ALREADY BEEN ARRESTED--BUT THERE'S THE LION NOW!

AS THE **BOY SPEEDSTER** GETS AN INSPIRATION...

INSTEAD OF TRYING TO BRING THE LION TO CAGE, I'LL BRING THE CAGE TO THE LION! WITH SUPER-SPEED, I CAN EASILY PUSH THIS HEAVY CAGE ALONG THE GROUND...

DEFTLY, BY THE USE OF HIS PHENOMENAL SPEED, **KID FLASH** TRAPS THE **KING OF BEASTS**...

GOT HIM! I MOVED SO FAST THE LION WAS INSIDE THE CAGE BEFORE IT EVEN KNEW WHAT WAS HAPPENING!

10

Then...

AND HERE'S THE BEAR! BOY, LISTEN TO THAT ANGRY GRUNT!

RRRR

*WHIRLING AROUND THE GREAT BEAST AT SUPER-SPEED, THE **BOY SPEEDSTER** CAUSES A CURRENT OF AIR TO SPIN MR. BRUIN LIKE A TOP...*

I'VE HEARD ABOUT **FLASH** DOING THIS--AND IT'S JUST AS EASY FOR ME!

MOMENTS AFTER, A TORNADO-LIKE FORCE BLOWS THE DAZED BEAR INTO ITS CAGE...

*AND SHORTLY AS ANOTHER **"CRIMSON COMET"** REACHES THE SCENE...*

AS SOON AS I HEARD THE NEWS OF THE ESCAPED ANIMALS, I CAME RIGHT OVER HERE-- BUT IT SEEMS THAT FOR ONCE **SOMEONE BEAT ME TO IT!**

KID FLASH GOT BOTH ANIMALS BACK SAFELY IN THEIR CAGES! GREAT JUPITER--! THIS IS A STRANGE FEELING I HAVE-- BUT A GOOD ONE--

I KNOW NOW THAT I WILL NEVER BE ALONE AGAIN IN MY STRUGGLE AGAINST EVIL AND INJUSTICE! I'VE GOT SOMEONE TO FIGHT AT MY SIDE-- **KID FLASH!** BUT I'D BETTER NOT LET HIM SEE ME... I WANT TO CHANGE BACK TO BARRY ALLEN...

11

LATER, AFTER *KID FLASH* TOO HAS SECRETLY CHANGED TO HIS CIVILIAN IDENTITY...AT BARRY'S APARTMENT...

I'M GLAD YOU HAD SUCH A FINE TIME WITH THE *FLASH,* WALLY! SORRY I--ER--HAD TO LEAVE...

THAT'S ALL RIGHT, MR. ALLEN! HERE COMES MY AUNT NOW--

WHEN IRIS HAS HEARD ABOUT THE DAY'S PROCEEDINGS...

WELL, MAYBE YOU'LL BE HAPPY NOW, WALLY--NOW THAT YOU'VE ACTUALLY MET THE *FLASH!* BUT TELL ME...

YOU SAY THAT *YOU* *KNOW* WHO THIS AMAZING NEW MARVEL-- *KID FLASH* IS--BUT YOU *CAN'T TELL ME*--OR BARRY HERE?

NO, AUNT IRIS, I *CAN'T*...

YOU SEE, IT'S SOMETHING THAT HAS TO BE A SECRET *FOREVER*...BETWEEN ME AND MY FRIEND, MR. FLASH!!

WATCH FOR ANOTHER EXCITING "KID FLASH" STORY IN A FUTURE ISSUE OF THE FLASH!

THE END 12

THE FLASH

WHERE DID THEY COME FROM? WHAT WAS THEIR MOTIVE IN ATTACKING THE EARTH? ONLY ONE MAN IN THE WORLD KNEW, AND LUCKILY FOR THE FATE OF EARTH THAT MAN WAS A PERSONAL FRIEND OF **BARRY** (THE FLASH) **ALLEN**-- WHO ALONE STOOD BETWEEN THE DREAD CREATURES AND THEIR COMPLETE DOMINATION OF THE PLANET!

The INVASION OF THE CLOUD CREATURES!

THIS CLOUD-HOPPING MANEUVER IS BRINGING ME WITHIN REACH OF THOSE EVIL **CLOUD CREATURES**-- WHERE I CAN STRIKE AT THEM!

"IT WAS TRUE MY PHOTO SHOWED NOTHING, AND YET.."

DID MY EYES SEE SOMETHING MY CAMERA COULDN'T? IS IT LIKE THE "CANALS" OF MARS THAT SOME ASTRONOMERS PROFESS TO SEE WITH THE NAKED EYE -- BUT CANNOT BE PHOTOGRAPHED?....

THE SAME COULD BE TRUE OF THE VOLCANO CREATURES I SAW! THIS PHOTO NEITHER PROVES -- NOR DISPROVES -- THEIR EXISTENCE!

"AS TIME WENT ON MY IDEAS ABOUT THE STRANGE BEINGS DEEPENED AND GREW... "

I'M CONVINCED NOW THAT A CIVILIZATION OF THE CREATURES EXISTS INSIDE THE EARTH -- AND THAT VOLCANOES AND EARTHQUAKES ARE THEIR ATTEMPTS TO ANNIHILATE US SURFACE CREATURES! ALTHOUGH I HAVE NO IDEA WHY!

SINCE NO OFFICIAL WOULD LISTEN TO ME, I DECIDED TO BRING MY THEORY BEFORE THE PUBLIC MYSELF -- IN THE FORM OF THESE LECTURES!

THAT'S WHY I'M HERE NOW, LADIES AND GENTLEMEN! I FEEL IT IS MY DUTY TO WARN THIS NATION THAT WE MAY BE IN GRAVE DANGER! IF I AM RIGHT, WE MUST BE ON OUR GUARD!

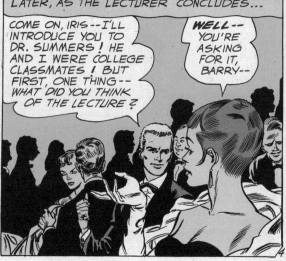

LATER, AS THE LECTURER CONCLUDES...

COME ON, IRIS -- I'LL INTRODUCE YOU TO DR. SUMMERS! HE AND I WERE COLLEGE CLASSMATES! BUT FIRST, ONE THING -- WHAT DID YOU THINK OF THE LECTURE?

WELL -- YOU'RE ASKING FOR IT, BARRY --

As PEAL AFTER PEAL OF THUNDER RENDS THE SURROUNDING AREA...

THE FORCE OF **SOUND** CAN SHATTER THE BUILDINGS OF THESE SURFACE CREATURES!

MAKE THE THUNDER LOUDER! **DESTROY!**

RRRRUGG!

IN NO TIME, EMERGENCY BROADCASTS FILL THE AIRWAVES OF THE NATION...

AND THE FANTASTIC INVADERS HAVE KNOCKED OUT ALL DEFENSE INSTALLATIONS IN THIS PART OF THE COUNTRY! NOTHING SEEMS CAPABLE OF STOPPING THEM!

"AND THOSE PLANES THAT SUCCEED IN GETTING OFF THE GROUND FIND THEIR ATTACKS FUTILE..."

IT'S LIKE FIRING AT A **PHANTOM!** TRYING TO DAMAGE THOSE CLOUD-THINGS, YOU CAN'T HIT ANYTHING!

MEANWHILE, BACK WITH DR. SUMMERS...

THESE ATTACKERS COULD BE THE **CLOUD CREATURES** I'VE TRIED TO WARN THE NATION AGAINST, MISS WEST!

UH-- WHERE'S BARRY? HE WAS HERE WITH US A MINUTE AGO--!

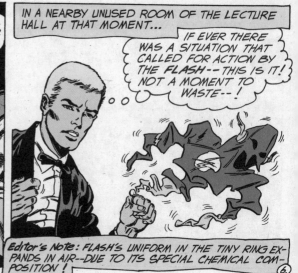

IN A NEARBY UNUSED ROOM OF THE LECTURE HALL AT THAT MOMENT...

IF EVER THERE WAS A SITUATION THAT CALLED FOR ACTION BY THE **FLASH** -- THIS IS IT! NOT A MOMENT TO WASTE--!

Editor's Note: FLASH'S UNIFORM IN THE TINY RING EXPANDS IN AIR--DUE TO ITS SPECIAL CHEMICAL COMPOSITION!

6.

AND SOON A FAMOUS SCARLET SHAPE WHIZZES THROUGH THE CITY...

THERE THEY ARE-- JUST AS DR. SUMMERS DESCRIBED THEM! AND... THEY'RE COMING AT ME!!

SOMEHOW THEY MUST HAVE LEARNED THAT I'M A *DANGER* TO THEM--AND ARE STARTING TO CONCENTRATE THEIR ATTACK ON *ME*!

AS TERRIBLE LIGHTNING BOLTS FLASH DOWN WITH LETHAL INTENT AT HIM, THE *FASTEST MAN ALIVE* PUTS ON A DAZZLING EXHIBITION...

THEY'RE TRYING TO *KNOCK ME OUT*--

--THE WAY THEY KNOCKED OUT OUR *DEFENSE INSTALLATIONS*!

I'M SAFE--AS LONG AS I CAN KEEP MOVING FASTER THAN THE DEADLY BOLTS!

WITH BLINDING SPEED, *FLASH* ESCAPES DESTRUCTION MOMENTARILY...

THEY SEEM TO BE CONFERRING UP THERE--PLANNING THEIR NEXT ATTACK ON ME! BUT WHY WAIT FOR THEM TO DEMOLISH ME-- WHEN I CAN LAUNCH AN ATTACK OF MY OWN!

THE NEXT INSTANT THE *KING OF SUPER-SPEED* BEGINS TO WHIRL IN A TIGHT CIRCLE...

I CAN'T FLY LIKE A BIRD! IN SPITE OF MY SPEED I'M BOUND BY *GRAVITY* JUST LIKE ANYONE ELSE! BUT STILL THERE'S A WAY OF GETTING AT THOSE CREATURES!

7

By circling round and round, *Flash* creates a *tornado*, the fiercest wind known...

I'm going to use this *tornado* as a weapon! Its wind can tear those creatures apart--and it reaches up high enough in the air--!

But moments later...

They simply increased their altitude--rose like clouds--a few hundred feet--and I *can't* get this tornado any higher!

Then, as if to reveal their own force to their scarlet-clad foe, the *cloud creatures* swoop down on a building...

Great Scott! They can do tricks with the air too! They've created a great vacuum--I can feel it from here! And by suction in the vacuum they're pulling that skyscraper right off the ground!

As the building is allowed to "crash-land" back to earth...

Lucky the occupants of the skyscraper vacated it in time! Meanwhile, I've come up with another plan to stop the *cloud creatures*...

8

SUDDENLY, FLASH STARTS OFF TOWARD A NEARBY HILL...

IF THIS MANEUVER STRIKES THEM AS FLEEING FROM BATTLE, THEY'LL SOON REALIZE THEIR MISTAKE...

SWIFT AS AN ANIMATED ELECTRON, THE FASTEST MAN ALIVE RACES UP THE HIGH HILL...

I'VE NOTICED ONE THING ABOUT THOSE TERRIBLE CLOUD-BEINGS--THEY EACH HAVE A CERTAIN DARK SPOT IN THEM--LIKE THE NUCLEUS OF A CELL--THE MOST VITAL PART...

...AND MY GUESS IS THAT DARK SPOT IS THE CENTER OF LIFE-- THE "HEART" OF THESE CREATURES! ANYWAY, IT'S THE PART I'VE GOT TO AIM FOR WHEN I REACH THEM...

AND THE WAY I'M GOING TO REACH THEM--OR PERISH IN THE ATTEMPT-- IS BY CLOUD-HOPPING!

EDITOR'S NOTE: FLASH'S PLAN TO REACH HIS DIABOLIC FOES IS BASED ON A FAMILIAR SCIENTIFIC PRINCIPLE! IF YOU DROP A FLAT STONE INTO WATER IT WILL SINK, BUT IF YOU SKIM IT ACROSS THE SURFACE LIKE THIS...

...IT WILL NOT SINK BUT KEEP GOING! IN THE SAME WAY FLASH'S IDEA IS THAT THE SOLID PARTICLES IN THE CLOUDS WILL SUSTAIN HIS SLIGHT WEIGHT AT SUPER-SPEED--AS HE SKIMS FROM THE SURFACE OF ONE CLOUD TO ANOTHER! BUT WILL IT WORK? LET'S FIND OUT ON THE NEXT PAGE FOLLOWING!

9

As the SCARLET SPEEDSTER reaches the summit...

THERE'S A CLOUD UP HERE LYING LOW ENOUGH SO THAT IT'S ALMOST TOUCHING THIS HILL TOP! I'VE GOT TO USE IT-- AND THE OTHER CLOUDS NEARBY-- TO REACH THOSE CREATURES!

WITH HIGH COURAGE, THE AMAZING FLASH WHIZZES OFF INTO NOTHINGNESS ... ONTO A CLOUD...

TOO EARLY YET TO SAY IF I'M GOING TO MAKE IT OR NOT...!

BUT THEN...

FALLING!! GOT TO INCREASE MY SPEED-- DRIVE MYSELF FORWARD...!

WITH EVERY OUNCE OF HIS ENERGY AND WILL, FLASH DRIVES HIS LEGS MORE FURIOUSLY...

I'M LEVELING OFF! NOW TO JUMP FROM THIS CLOUD TO THE NEXT ONE...

As the INCREDIBLE HUMAN PROJECTILE COMPLETES THE SKIPPING MANEUVER FROM ONE CLOUD TO THE NEXT...

HERE I GO--

CLOSER AND CLOSER--

TO THOSE CLOUD CREATURES!

10

CALLING UPON HIS ULTIMATE RESERVES, THE GREAT SPEEDSTER REACHES AN UNBELIEVABLE VELOCITY THROUGH THE AIR...

MY SPEED IS PROPELLING ME RIGHT THROUGH IT!

ROCKETING AT THE LAST OF THE CLOUD CREATURES...

GOT IT!

THE NEXT INSTANT...

BUT I'M NOT DOWN TO EARTH YET! I COULDN'T SURVIVE A STRAIGHT FALL FROM THIS HEIGHT--SO THE THING TO DO IS TO KEEP WORKING FOR SPEED-- TO PREVENT MY DESCENT FROM BEING TOO SUDDEN!

WITH HIS INCREDIBLE SPEED, FLASH MANAGES TO GET ENOUGH SUPPORT OUT OF THE AIR ITSELF TO LAND SAFELY ON AN INCLINE...

GOT TO BRAKE HARD-- OR MY MOMENTUM WILL CRASH ME INTO THAT FARMHOUSE!

AND FROM ABOVE, AFTER THE FASTEST MAN ALIVE HAS STOPPED...

WATER--A DOWNPOUR! IT'S THOSE CREATURES -- IN PERISHING, THEY SIMPLY TURNED TO WATER--JUST LIKE REAL CLOUDS TURN TO RAIN!

LATER, WITH THE DANGER PAST, DR. WILEY SUMMERS ADDRESSES THE NATION VIA *TV* AND RADIO...

AND THANKS TO *FLASH*, WE NO LONGER HAVE TO WORRY ABOUT THE *CLOUD CREATURES!* THEY MIGHT HAVE WON CONTROL OF EARTH-- WHICH WAS THEIR AIM!--BY THEIR FIRST SURPRISE ATTACK! BUT NOW THAT THAT HAS BEEN BEATEN...

...WE WILL BE READY FOR ANY FURTHER INVASION...SHOULD THEY EVER TRY AGAIN!

I'VE SURE CHANGED MY MIND ABOUT DR. SUMMERS SINCE BARRY INTRODUCED ME TO HIM!

AFTER THE BROADCAST, IRIS WEST RECEIVES A PHONE CALL...

A DATE WITH YOU TONIGHT, BARRY? I'M SORRY, I ALREADY HAVE A DATE-- WITH DR. SUMMERS! YES, I FIND HIM BRILLIANT-- ABSOLUTELY FASCINATING...

SHE QUOTED MY ORIGINAL WORDS ABOUT DR. SUMMERS-- RIGHT BACK AT ME! Hmm... LOOKS LIKE I MAY HAVE A RIVAL FOR IRIS'S AFFECTION!

The End

13

The FLASH presents... KID FLASH

WALLY WEST--ALIAS THE AMAZING KID FLASH--HAS HIS HANDS FULL WHEN A GANG OF HARD-HEADED "CATS" BANDS TOGETHER TO "RUMBLE" WITH A RIVAL GANG!

AND WHEN THE GANG-WAR EXPLODES INTO FIERY ACTION, KID FLASH TURNS ON THE STEAM TO BEAT OFF...

The CHALLENGE OF THE CRIMSON CROWS!

As YOUNG WALLY WEST AWAKES ONE MORNING IN HIS HOME TOWN OF *BLUE VALLEY*...

JUMPIN' JETS! WHAT A DREAM I HAD LAST NIGHT! IT WAS AS IF EVERY WISH I'VE EVER HAD CAME TRUE ALL AT ONCE! FIRST OF ALL I DREAMED I MET MY IDOL, *FLASH*, FACE TO FACE...!

AND NOT ONLY THAT, BUT IN MY DREAM AS *FLASH* WAS SHOWING ME THE EXPERIMENT THAT ACCIDENTALLY LED TO HIS AMAZING SPEED--A FANTASTIC THING HAPPENED...

ANOTHER LIGHTNING BOLT... SPILLING CHEMICALS OVER THE BOY--IN THE SAME WAY IT DID TO *ME* YEARS AGO--AND GAVE ME, MY SUPER-SPEED!

"ON *FLASH'S* HUNCH WE HAD A LITTLE RACE, HE AND I!"

I'M IN SUPER-SPEED NOW-- BUT H-HE'S KEEPING UP WITH ME! THERE'S NO DOUBT OF IT! WALLY NOW HAS THE *SPEED OF LIGHT*!

"IT WAS *FLASH* HIMSELF WHO OUTFITTED ME SOON AFTER WITH MY UNIFORM ...AND A CERTAIN RING ... "

THAT'S IT, WALLY! WHEN YOU PRESS THE HIDDEN SPRING ON THE RING, YOUR UNIFORM WILL SHOOT OUT--JUST LIKE MINE DOES! BUT YOU MUST BE CAREFUL ...

AS *KID FLASH*--THE NAME I HAVE GIVEN YOU--YOU MUST USE YOUR SPEED ONLY TO COMBAT EVIL AND TO HELP THOSE IN DISTRESS --AND NEVER FOR YOUR OWN PERSONAL GAIN!

I--I UNDERSTAND, MR. FLASH!

A SPLIT-SECOND LATER...

BLUE VALLEY HIGH SCHOOL

BONG!

I RAN... ALL THE WAY... IN LESS TIME THAN IT TOOK THE SCHOOL BELL TO FINISH RINGING! GREAT SATELLITES! IT MUST MEAN THAT--

AS WALLY FILES INTO SCHOOL...

WHAT I THOUGHT WAS A DREAM--WAS NO DREAM AT ALL! THERE'S ONE SURE WAY TO PROVE IT...

ON IMPULSE, THE LAD STICKS HIS HAND INTO HIS POCKET AND...

THE RING FLASH GAVE ME--THE ONE WITH THE HIDDEN KID FLASH UNIFORM IN IT!

ROOM 4!

FILLED WITH HIS HEART-POUNDING SECRET, WALLY TAKES HIS PLACE IN THE CLASSROOM..

IT'S A GOOD THING NO ONE SEEMED TO NOTICE ME ON MY AMAZING RUN HERE! I RACED SO FAST, NO HUMAN EYE COULD SEE ME!

NO ONE MUST EVER SUSPECT THAT WALLY WEST AND KID FLASH ARE ONE AND THE SAME PERSON! IF IT GOT OUT, EVIL-DOERS MIGHT TRY TO TAKE ADVANTAGE...

LATER, IN THE SCHOOL GYMNASIUM...

AND YET IT'S AWFULLY HARD TO KEEP DOWN MY SENSE OF EXCITEMENT! WHAT WOULD THE FELLERS SAY IF THEY KNEW I WAS KID FLASH?!

4.

IN THE BASKETBALL GAME THAT FOLLOWS...

COME ON, WALLY! WE NEED ONE MORE BASKET TO WIN!

THE FOLLOWING MOMENT...

WOW! DID YA SEE HOW FAST WALLY DRIBBLED PAST HIS OPPONENT?

THROUGH THE ENTIRE RIVAL TEAM STREAKS A DAZZLING FIGURE!...

AND AT THE END OF THE COURT...

WALLY WON THE GAME FOR US!

BUT AFTERWARDS AS WALLY IS CALLED UPON TO EXPLAIN HIS "FAST DRIBBLE"...

IT'S--ER--SOMETHING I'VE BEEN SECRETLY PRACTICING, FELLOWS!

I FORGOT MY-SELF IN THE EXCITEMENT OF THE GAME! I'VE GOT TO BE MORE CAREFUL IN THE FUTURE!

LATER, AFTER SCHOOL...

THERE'S THOSE KIDS WHO CALL THEMSELVES THE *CRIMSON CROWS!* MOST OF THEM ARE FRIENDS OF MINE -- AND THEY'VE BEEN TRYING TO GET ME TO JOIN THEIR GANG ...

BUT I CAN'T GO FOR THE THINGS THEY DO! I THINK THEY'RE HEADING FOR *TROUBLE* ...

HI, WALLY!

HI, STEVE! WHAT ARE YOU CATS UP TO?

CAN'T SPILL IT, WALLY-- 'CAUSE YOU'RE NOT "WITH" US! WE'RE GONNA HOLD A *SECRET MEETING* TODAY...

TIME FOR THE MEETING! BLOW THE *CROW SIGNAL!*

CAW! CAW! CAW!

HA! I MADE YOU "CHICKEN OUT," GEORGIE!

THESE KIDS THINK THEY'RE HOT STUFF WITH THEIR *CROW SIGNAL* -- AND THE SOUPED-UP BICYCLES THEY RIDE AND PLAY "CHICKEN" WITH EACH OTHER!

IF I'M GOING TO HELP THOSE FELLOWS AND KEEP THEM OUT OF *REAL TROUBLE*, I'VE GOT TO KNOW WHAT THEY'RE UP TO!

DOOR CLOSING--

WITH A BLURRING BURST OF SUPER-SPEED, *KID FLASH* GAINS THE SHACK...

JUST MADE IT! AND THE *CROWS* DON'T SUSPECT I'M HERE!

MOVING TOO FAST TO BE SEEN BY THE NAKED EYE, THE BOY SPEEDSTER WHIRLS AROUND THE CLUBROOM...

HEY, DO YOU FEEL A DRAFT IN HERE?

DON'T BE A DRAG, DAD! THE DOOR'S CLOSED, ISN'T IT? LET'S GET DOWN TO BUSINESS!

RIGHT! YOU ALL KNOW WHY YOU'RE HERE, *CROWS*...!

LAST WEEK WE HAD A *RUMBLE* WITH OUR RIVALS, THE *GOLDEN EAGLES!* THEY WON! BUT HERE'S HOW WE EVEN THE SCORE...

CRIMSON CROWS

WE'RE GONNA BLOW UP A STORM--SMASH THEIR CLUBHOUSE TO THE GROUND! ALL IN FAVOR SAY *CAW!*

CAW! CAW!

WITH A TERRIFIC BURST OF SUPER-SPEED, *KID FLASH* CREATES A *FIREBREAK* BEFORE THE CHARGING FLAMES, BY SCYTHING TREES DOWN WITH HIS BARE HANDS!...

ORDINARILY I COULDN'T CUT DOWN SMALL TREES THIS WAY... BUT AT SUPER-SPEED I DON'T EVEN FEEL IT AS THE PALM OF MY HAND SLICES THROUGH THESE THIN TREE-TRUNKS!*

*Editor's Note: IN A SIMILAR WAY, A SINGLE STRAW HAS BEEN DRIVEN *TWO FEET* INTO SOLID OAK BY THE SPEED OF TORNADO WINDS!

BUT MOMENTS LATER...

JUMPING JETS! THE FIRE IS LEAPING ACROSS THE *FIREBREAK* I MADE TO HOLD IT BACK!

ONLY ONE POSSIBLE WAY TO STOP IT NOW!

WHIRLING AT EVEN GREATER SPEED THAN BEFORE, KID FLASH SETS UP A *COUNTERWIND* TO DRIVE BACK THE FLAMES!...

FOREST RANGERS SOMETIMES BUILD ONE FIRE TO FIGHT ANOTHER ONE -- A *BACKFIRE!* BUT I THINK MY WAY IS QUICKER AND SAFER...

10

AROUND AND AROUND THE FLAME AREA WHIZZES THE **BOY JETSTER** TO KEEP THE FIRE CONTAINED...

THE FIRE'S NOT SPREADING ANY MORE! IT'S BURNING ITSELF OUT!

AS THE LAST EMBERS DIE AWAY...

BOY--ARE WE LUCKY THE WIND CHANGED WHEN IT DID!

THEY DON'T REALIZE IT, BUT **I** WAS THAT WIND!

AT LEAST THE EXCITEMENT COOLED OFF THAT RUMBLE!

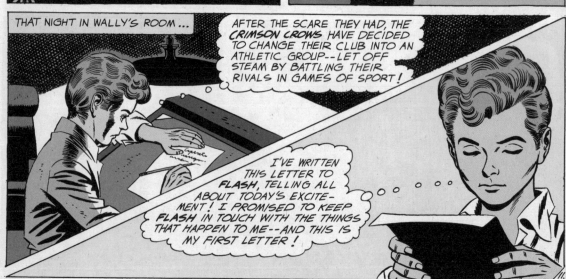

THAT NIGHT IN WALLY'S ROOM...

AFTER THE SCARE THEY HAD, THE **CRIMSON CROWS** HAVE DECIDED TO CHANGE THEIR CLUB INTO AN ATHLETIC GROUP--LET OFF STEAM BY BATTLING THEIR RIVALS IN GAMES OF SPORT!

I'VE WRITTEN THIS LETTER TO **FLASH**, TELLING ALL ABOUT TODAY'S EXCITEMENT! I PROMISED TO KEEP FLASH IN TOUCH WITH THE THINGS THAT HAPPEN TO ME--AND THIS IS MY FIRST LETTER!

11.

I'VE ADDRESSED IT CARE OF BARRY ALLEN, IN CENTRAL CITY! IT WAS AT MR. ALLEN'S HOUSE -- WHERE MY AUNT IRIS TOOK ME -- THAT I MET FLASH IN PERSON!

MR. ALLEN TOLD ME THAT HE HAD A CERTAIN ROOM WHICH FLASH OCCASIONALLY VISITS AND WHERE HE CAN RECEIVE MAIL! HE'LL GET THIS TOMORROW -- WAIT!!

IT JUST OCCURRED TO ME! BY SUPER-SPEED I CAN DELIVER THIS LETTER MYSELF -- IN LESS TIME THAN IT WOULD TAKE THE LETTER TO FALL TO THE BOTTOM OF THIS MAIL BOX!

AS THOUGHT BECOMES ACTION AND THE BOY PHENOMENON ROCKETS OFF...

I'M ALMOST IN CENTRAL CITY! ANOTHER SPLIT-INSTANT AND I'LL BE AT MR. ALLEN'S APARTMENT!

THEN...

THERE! NOW TO GET HOME AND INTO BED! I'VE HAD A LONG DAY... AND I'M TIRED!

AND THAT VERY NIGHT FLASH READS HIS MAIL...

I'M GLAD TO SEE THAT WALLY IS USING HIS SUPER-SPEED TO HELP OTHERS -- AND NOT FOR HIS OWN GAIN! IT PROVES HE'S THE RIGHT BOY TO BE MY PROTÉGÉ!

THE END

WATCH FOR ANOTHER FAST-MOVING ADVENTURE WITH KID FLASH IN A FORTH-COMING ISSUE!

133

THE FLASH

WHETHER HE WAS AWAKE--OR ASLEEP--THE *FLASH* KEPT RUNNING INTO HIS ARCHRIVAL-- THE INCREDIBLE MAN WITH THE FANTASTIC ABILITY TO STRETCH HIS BODY TO UN- LIMITED LENGTHS!
WHO WAS THIS ASTOUNDING CREATURE-- AND WHAT WAS HIS CONNECTION WITH CERTAIN MYSTERIOUS EVENTS OCCURRING IN *CENTRAL CITY?* THE *WORLD'S FASTEST HUMAN*--FOR HIS OWN PEACE OF MIND--HAD TO SOLVE ...

The MYSTERY of the ELONGATED MAN!

THE *ELONGATED MAN*-- HE'S AHEAD OF ME IN OUR MATCH RACE, EVEN THOUGH HIS FEET HAVEN'T LEFT THE STARTING LINE!

FASCINATED, THE CROWD SWARMS ABOUT THE NEWCOMER...

WELL, THIS IS A NEW EXPERIENCE FOR ME! I'M BEING *IGNORED*-- WHILE IRIS AND THOSE OTHER PEOPLE FLOCK AROUND THAT *ELONGATED MAN!*

LATER THAT WEEK IN THE APARTMENT OF BARRY ALLEN, ALIAS THE *FLASH*...

THE *ELONGATED MAN* AGAIN! THE PAPERS ARE FULL OF HIM--AND HIS PICTURES TOO! HE SURE IS STEALING *FLASH'S* THUNDER!

WHY, ONLY YESTERDAY...

"... I WAS STROLLING ALONG THE RIVERFRONT WHEN I HEARD A CALL FOR HELP FROM THE NEARBY DOCKS..."

HELP!

SOUNDS LIKE SOMEONE'S IN *TROUBLE!*

"BEFORE THE CALL FOR HELP HAD FADED AWAY, A SECRET SPRING HAD BEEN PRESSED ON MY RING... MY *FLASH* UNIFORM HAD SPURTED OUT, EXPANDING INSTANTLY ON CONTACT WITH AIR...

"BUT IN THE SPLIT-SECOND IT TOOK ME TO 'FLASH' TO THE DOCKS..."

SCOOPED AGAIN-- BY THE *ELONGATED MAN!*

HOLD ON! I'LL PULL YOU UP TO SAFETY!

3

AND HE SEEMS TO BE ON THE SPOT *ESPECIALLY* WHEN *FLASH* IS IN THE VICINITY! IT'S AS IF HE WANTS TO ROB HIM OF POPULARITY--OR TO ECLIPSE HIM IN THE PUBLIC EYE! Hmmm... I CAN'T HELP WONDERING...

WHO *IS* THE *ELONGATED MAN* REALLY? AND HOW DID HE GET THAT SPECIAL *ABILITY* OF HIS-- THAT ENABLES HIM TO STRETCH HIMSELF SO FANTASTICALLY?

SO... YOU WISH TO KNOW ABOUT *FLASH'S* RIVAL, EH, BARRY? WELL, THAT'S AN UNDERSTANDABLE DESIRE! ACTUALLY, THE FACTS ABOUT THE *ELONGATED MAN* ARE *NOT* SO EXTRAORDINARY AS YOU MIGHT IMAGINE! FOR EXAMPLE, HE WAS BORN...

...RALPH DIBNY, THE SECOND SON OF AN AVERAGE MIDWEST AMERICAN FAMILY! ONE DAY WHEN HE WAS NINE YEARS OLD, HIS PARENTS TOOK HIM TO A TRAVELING SIDE-SHOW...

JIMINY PETE! LOOK AT THAT MAN TWIST HIMSELF AROUND-- LIKE A PRETZEL!

INDIA RUBBER MAN

COME ON, RALPH! THERE'S OTHER THINGS TO SEE HERE!

LEMME ALONE! I'M GONNA STAY HERE AND WATCH HIM SOME MORE!

RALPH JUST COULDN'T GET ENOUGH OF THE *INDIA RUBBER MAN!* AT THE END OF THE SHOW...

GINGOLD SODA WATER

EXCUSE ME, MISTER INDIA RUBBER MAN-- BUT COULD YOU TELL ME *HOW* YOU STRETCH YOURSELF THAT WAY?

SORRY, YOUNG FELLER... BUT I CAN'T TELL YOU! YOU SEE-- IT'S A *TRADE SECRET!*

OH!

4

138

WHEN RALPH WENT HOME AT THE END OF THE DAY, HE **KNEW** WHAT HIS AMBITION IN LIFE WAS...

I'VE NEVER **SEEN** ANYTHING SO EXCITING AS THAT **INDIA RUBBER MAN!** AND SOMEHOW... SOMEWAY... **I'M GONNA LEARN** THAT **SECRET**... OF HOW TO STRETCH MYSELF OUT!

AS RALPH DIBNY GREW UP HE CARRIED OUT HIS RESOLUTION...

I'VE VISITED **FIVE** INDIA RUBBER MEN IN SIDESHOWS ALL OVER THE COUNTRY... BUT **NONE** OF THEM SEEMS TO BE ABLE... OR TO WANT TO TELL ME... HOW HE DOES IT!

AT THE END OF A DISAPPOINTING YEAR...

I'M BEGINNING TO THINK THAT THERE **IS NO SECRET**-- HOW THEY DO IT! I THINK THAT FIRST ONE LONG AGO WAS JUST HAVING A **JOKE** AT MY EXPENSE!

HE DIDN'T REALIZE HE WAS PUTTING ME ON A TRAIL THAT'S TAKEN **ALL MY LIFE!** FOR NOTHING! BUT WAIT A SECOND... I JUST THOUGHT OF SOMETHING! GOLLY, IT JUST POPPED INTO MY HEAD --

WHAT RALPH DIBNY THOUGHT OF, AND SUDDENLY REMEMBERED, WAS THIS...

-- THAT IN **EVERY** INDIA RUBBER MAN'S TENT WHERE HE HAD GONE, THERE HAD BEEN A BOTTLE OF A SOFT DRINK CALLED **GINGOLD!** BUT-- WHAT DID **THAT** MEAN?

I'VE FOUND OUT... THAT THE **INDIA RUBBER MEN DON'T DRINK GINGOLD** BECAUSE THEY THINK IT WILL MAKE THEM STRETCHIER-- BUT ONLY BECAUSE THEY HAPPEN TO LIKE IT! BUT IF THEY **ALL** LIKE IT, ISN'T THAT SOME KIND OF **CLUE?**

BUT WHAT **WAS** RALPH DIBNY'S AMBITION? THAT REMAINS FOR **FLASH** TO PUZZLE OUT!

THERE'S SOMETHING ABOUT THIS...**ELONGATED MAN**! EVER SINCE HE CAME TO **CENTRAL CITY** CERTAIN PECULIAR THINGS HAVE HAPPENED THAT POINT A **FINGER OF SUSPICION** AT HIM!

THERE WAS THIS CASE A COUPLE OF DAYS AGO! AN **OUTSIDE WINDOW** WAS FORCED ON THE TWENTIETH FLOOR OF A SKYSCRAPER IN MIDTOWN, AND A SAFE INSIDE LOOTED! THE WALL WAS SHEER...

DAILY EXP

ELONGATED MAN AGAIN

"BUT THE ELONGATED MAN COULD HAVE REACHED DOWN FROM THE ROOF DURING THE NIGHT..."

"...AND EASILY PULLED THE JOB!"

AND THAT'S NOT THE ONLY ONE! THERE WERE OTHER ROBBERIES OF THE SAME **MYSTERIOUS** KIND... EH? MY PHONE!

RING!

HELLO!

IT'S IRIS!

GOOD GOSH! DID I HAVE A DATE WITH HER-- THAT I'VE FORGOTTEN ABOUT--?

/7

BARRY--I JUST WANTED TO TELL YOU--

SHE'S GOING TO BAWL ME OUT FOR BEING *LATE* AGAIN...

...IF YOU SEE YOUR FRIEND *FLASH*--WOULD YOU PASS ON A FRIENDLY *WARNING* TO HIM FROM ME?

HUH--?

TELL HIM HE MAY NOT WIN THE *MAN OF THE YEAR* AWARD THIS YEAR! THE *ELONGATED MAN* IS A STRONG CONTENDER-- AND COULD BEAT HIM OUT FOR THE *HONOR*!

OH!

AFTER IRIS HAS HUNG UP...

SO? THE *ELONGATED MAN* AGAIN! AND HE'S THREATENING TO BEAT OUT *FLASH* FOR THE *MAN OF THE YEAR* AWARD? WELL... WE'LL SEE ABOUT *THAT*!

MOMENTS LATER, THE *FASTEST MAN ON EARTH* ROCKETS ACROSS *CENTRAL CITY*...

I HAVE AN IDEA...

...THAT WILL NOT ONLY PREVENT THE *ELONGATED MAN* FROM WINNING ANY SUCH HONOR...

...BUT WILL EXPOSE HIM FOR WHAT HE *REALLY* IS!

18

SOON... IN THE OFFICE OF THE SINORIENT IMPORTING COMPANY...

YES, IT IS TRUE, *FLASH*-- WE WERE GOING TO *POSTPONE* OUR EXHIBITION OF MING VASES --DUE TO THE WAVE OF MYSTERIOUS ROBBERIES IN TOWN--!

YES, I KNOW-- --THROUGH MY IDENTITY AS BARRY ALLEN, RESEARCH SCIENTIST AT POLICE HEAD-QUARTERS!

BUT I'VE COME HERE, GENTLE-MEN, TO URGE YOU TO DO *NO SUCH THING!*

WHAT?! YOU ASK US TO TAKE A RISK? DO YOU REALIZE, *FLASH*, THAT THIS POTTERY--FROM THE FIFTEENTH CENTURY--THE MING DYNASTY IN CHINA -- IS PRACTICALLY *PRICELESS* ?

I DO! BUT LISTEN --

IT'S OUR *BEST WAY* OF TRAPPING THE ELUSIVE ROBBER! AND AS FOR YOUR POTTERY, *I MYSELF* WILL UNDER-TAKE TO *GUARANTEE* ITS SAFETY!

WELL, IN *THAT* CASE...!

AT THE EXHIBITION HALL, SHORTLY, THE WORLD'S MOST WONDERFUL *WATCHMAN* GOES ON DUTY...

AT SUPER-SPEED I'M *INVISIBLE*... AND I CAN COVER...

...EVERY ONE OF THESE *EXIT DOORS*--

...SIMULTANEOUSLY! AND TO PLAY IT SAFE...

I'M STARTING MY ROUNDS EVEN *BEFORE* THEY PUT THE *VASES* OUT HERE!

THE *ELONGATED MAN* DOESN'T REALIZE IT, BUT I'M SETTING A *TRAP* FOR HIM ! HE'S SURE TO HAVE READ ABOUT THIS EXHIBITION --AND IF I'M RIGHT, HE'LL BE HERE --EH ?

FLASH-- *WHERE* ARE YOU--?

AS THE SCARLET SPEEDSTER APPLIES THE BRAKES..

OH, *FLASH*--THE MOST TERRIBLE THING ! THE PRECIOUS VASES-- THEY'VE BEEN STOLEN FROM THE WAREHOUSE NEXT DOOR-- *BEFORE* WE COULD EVEN PUT THEM ON DISPLAY HERE !

GREAT SCOTT !

LIKE CRIMSON LIGHTNING, FLASH DARTS TOWARD THE SCENE OF THE CRIME...

THE *ELONGATED MAN* ! I'VE CAUGHT YOU RED-HANDED !

FLASH-- AFTER *ME* ??

AS THE *ELONGATED MAN* RACES OFF...

GOT TO GET AWAY--!

I'LL PROVE HE'S NO MATCH FOR ME !

GOT HIM !

BY STRETCHING MYSELF AROUND THIS TREE, I CAN GRAB THE *FLASH* !

BUT NOT EVEN THE *ELONGATED MAN* CAN OUTSPEED THE *WORLD'S FASTEST MAN...*

NOW-- *WHERE* ARE THOSE VASES ?

IN THE GARAGE BEHIND THE WAREHOUSE-- WHERE I PUT THEM !

I PUT THEM HERE SO THEY'D BE SAFE--AFTER I TOOK THEM FROM THE CROOKS!

FROM-- *WHAT* CROOKS?!

IN AN ADJOINING GARAGE...

HERE THEY ARE! I LOCKED THEM IN HERE-- AND I WAS GOING FOR THE POLICE WHEN YOU-- ER--STOPPED ME!

GREAT STARS! AND I THOUGHT THAT *YOU* WERE THE GUILTY PARTY--

AS MATTERS GET CLEARED UP...

THEN YOU CAME HERE *EARLY* IN ORDER TO CAPTURE THESE ROBBERS --AND *CLEAR YOUR GOOD NAME?*

WHICH IS RALPH DIBNY, BY THE WAY! YES, I DID, *FLASH*...

YOU SEE, WHEN I REALIZED I HAD THIS AMAZING TALENT TO STRETCH MYSELF, I VOWED I WOULD ONLY USE MY ABILITY IN EMERGENCIES OR TO HELP PEOPLE! BUT THESE THIEVES WERE MAKING IT LOOK AS IF *I* WERE THE *CULPRIT*...

...COMMITTING THE MYSTERIOUS CRIMES! SO I HAD TO TRY TO CLEAR MYSELF!

SAY-- I *RECOGNIZE* THOSE MEN...! THEY BELONG TO THE *PERRY VETO* GANG! BUT WHERE'S THE RINGLEADER?

THERE *WAS* A THIRD MAN--BUT HE ESCAPED ME, *FLASH!*

THAT *MUST* HAVE BEEN *PERRY VETO* HIMSELF! GOT TO TRACK HIM DOWN--

As FLASH embarks on a SUPER-SPEED MANHUNT...

PERRY VETO IS THE MOST WANTED CRIMINAL IN THE STATE! BUT SO FAR HE'S MANAGED TO ELUDE CAPTURE--EH?

MARKS OF A CAR HERE--

--THAT TOOK OFF SO QUICKLY THE TIRES LEFT RUBBER MARKS ON THE ROAD! PERRY VETO MUST HAVE BEEN IN THAT CAR!

AS THE WORLD'S FASTEST HUMAN TRAILS THE GETAWAY CAR BY HIS OWN UNIQUE METHODS...

NO SIGN THIS WAY...

OR THIS WAY...

HERE'S SOME-THING... THOSE TIRE MARKS AGAIN!

AND SOON, AS THE EARTH'S SWIFTEST PURSUER GAINS SIGHT OF HIS QUARRY...

THERE IT IS--AND JUST AS I SUSPECTED, IT'S PERRY VETO AT THE WHEEL!

WITH AN EXTRA BURST OF SPEED, FLASH "DETAINS" THE CROOK...

THIS IS ONE WAY TO STOP THE CAR! BY RAPIDLY CIRCLING AROUND IT, I'VE CREATED A SUCTION THAT HAS RAISED THE CAR OFF THE ROAD!

12

146

As the speedster seizes the gang chief...

BETTER BUTTON UP YOUR OVERCOAT, *VETO!* YOU MAY FIND IT *WINDY* ON THIS *SUPER-SWIFT* TRIP TO POLICE HEAD-QUARTERS!

Later, in the office of the police chief...

VETO HAS CONFESSED, *FLASH*-- THAT HE AND HIS GANG COMMITTED THOSE *"MYSTERIOUS"* CRIMES WITH THE AID OF A *HELICOPTER!*

THEY FIGURED THAT THE *ELONGATED MAN* WOULD BE SUSPECTED-- AND THAT WOULD LEAVE THEM IN THE CLEAR!

BUT THANKS TO YOU, *FLASH*-- THEY'RE *IN THE CLEAR!*

Some days later at a SPECIAL CEREMONY arranged by PICTURE NEWS...

...AND WE ANNOUNCE A *TIE* FOR THE *MAN OF THE YEAR AWARD!* *FLASH* AND THE *ELONGATED MAN* DIVIDE THE HONOR!

HOW ABOUT THE TWO OF THEM SHAKING HANDS?

RIGHT! JUST SIT WHERE YOU ARE, *FLASH*--

¡Whew!¡ TALK ABOUT A *"BOARDINGHOUSE REACH"!* RALPH, I'D SURE LIKE YOU WITH ME AT ALL BANQUETS I ATTEND THIS SEASON!

ANYTIME, *FLASH*-- ANYTIME!

The End

13

In BLUE VALLEY PUBLIC SCHOOL, LINDA GRANT, PRETTY AND POPULAR YOUNG TEACHER, ADDRESSES HER CLASS BEFORE THE SUMMER VACATION...

WELL, BOYS AND GIRLS, THIS IS THE END OF THE SCHOOL TERM-- AND THE LAST DAY YOU'LL SPEND IN THIS OLD SCHOOL BUILDING! WHEN YOU RETURN IN THE FALL...

...YOU'LL COME TO THE NEW BUILDING! HERE'S A PICTURE OF WHAT IT'S GOING TO LOOK LIKE...

OOH!

SUPER! COOL!

AND NOW, GOODBY, CLASS! I'LL SEE YOU IN SEPTEMBER!

AS THE CLASS FILES OUT, INCLUDING WALLY WEST-- WHOSE SECRET IDENTITY IS THE AMAZING KID FLASH...

EVERYBODY IN OUR CLASS LIKES MISS GRANT-- SHE'S SO PRETTY... AND LIVELY! BUT SOMEHOW... SHE DOESN'T SEEM HER- SELF TODAY!

CURIOUSLY, FOR A MOMENT, WALLY LINGERS IN THE DOORWAY, AND SEES...

JUMPING JETS! SHE'S CRYING!

ON IMPULSE, THE ALERT LAD RETURNS...

MISS GRANT, IS THERE SOMETHING WRONG? I COULDN'T HELP NOTICING...

OH, WALLY! I DIDN'T MEAN FOR ANYONE TO SEE, BUT SINCE YOU'VE ASKED ME...

AS WORDS AND TEARS TUMBLE FROM THE PRETTY TEACHER...

RALPH PARKER, THE CITY **YOUTH ADVISER**, AND I ARE ENGAGED TO BE MARRIED--

YES, MISS GRANT! ALL THE KIDS IN TOWN KNOW THAT!

WELL, MR. PARKER IS IN THE CONSTRUCTION BUSINESS, AND HE SUBMITTED A BID TO BUILD THE NEW SCHOOL! HE WANTED SO MUCH TO GET THE CONTRACT, HE ENTERED AN ESPECIALLY LOW BID ...

...BUT AN OUT-OF-TOWN FIRM PUT IN AN EVEN **LOWER** BID AND WON THE CONTRACT! THEY'RE THE ONES WHO ARE ERECTING THE NEW BUILDING NOW...

NATURALLY RALPH AND I FELT BAD, WALLY! AND NOW, THINKING OF THE NEW SCHOOL MADE ME THINK OF OUR DISAPPOINTMENT! WE'VE EVEN HAD TO POSTPONE OUR MARRIAGE!

GOSH, MISS GRANT, I'M SORRY...

OUTSIDE, AFTER THE TEACHER HAS RE-COVERED HER COMPOSURE...

'BYE NOW, WALLY-- AND THANKS FOR YOUR SYMPATHY!

SO LONG, MISS GRANT! I HOPE THINGS TURN OUT ALL RIGHT...

I SURE WISH I COULD DO SOMETHING TO HELP MISS GRANT AND MR. PARKER! THEY'RE BOTH SO NICE-- AND IT DOES SEEM A SHAME MR. PARKER DIDN'T GET THAT CONTRACT!

ON HIS WAY HOME, WALLY PASSES THE CONSTRUCTION SITE OF THE NEW SCHOOL ...

ACCORDING TO MISS GRANT, THE **BIG ACE CONSTRUCTION COMPANY** HAS CONTRACTED TO FINISH THE NEW BUILDING BEFORE SEPTEMBER ! THAT SURE IS **FAST GOING** -- SINCE THEY STARTED ONLY TWO MONTHS AGO !

SHORTLY, SOME BLOCKS AWAY...

I GUESS RALPH PARKER COULDN'T MATCH THAT SPEED, AND THAT MUST BE ONE REASON HE DIDN'T -- EH?.?

SLUG HIM, DOBY !

JUMPING JETS ! TWO THUGS -- ATTACKING RALPH PARKER ! LOOKS LIKE HE COULD USE THE HELP OF **KID FLASH** !

CONCEALED IN SHADOW, WALLY PRESSES A HIDDEN SPRING ON HIS RING, AND INSTANTLY...

BY A SECRET CHEMICAL FORMULA, WALLY'S **KID FLASH** UNIFORM EXPANDS ENORMOUSLY IN THE AIR AS IT SPURTS FROM HIS RING!

THEN...A BRIGHT SCARLET SHAPE WHIZZES TOWARD THE UNEQUAL CONFLICT...

MR. PARKER COULD PROBABLY HANDLE THOSE MUGGERS ONE AT A TIME, BUT BOTH TOGETHER--

DOBY, LOOK--

WHAT IN BLAZES--?

GOT TO USE SOME SPEED-STUNTS TO DRIVE THOSE THUGS OFF--

4

BY WHIRLING ROUND AND AROUND HIS FOES, THE *FASTEST BOY ALIVE* SETS UP A *WIND ACTION* THAT SENDS THE THUGS REELING...

I'VE SEEN MY IDOL...

...THE *FLASH* DO THIS! THE WIND...

...SET UP BY MY *SUPER-SPEED* CAN BE AS...

...*POWERFUL AS A HURRICANE!*

AS THE WIND SENDS THE ASSAILANTS *RUNNING*...

I'M *FORCING* THEM TO *RUN* -- IN ORDER TO KEEP FROM FALLING! THEY CAN'T HELP THEMSELVES!

MOMENTS LATER...

PUFF! WHAT *WAS* THAT?

I DUNNO -- AND I'M TOO POOPED TO TRY AND FIND OUT!

AS *KID FLASH* REJOINS THE MAN HE RESCUED...

MR. PARKER! ARE YOU ALL RIGHT?

YES! BUT -- YOU CAN'T BE THE FAMOUS *FLASH*.. YOU'RE TOO SMALL!

STARTLED, RALPH PARKER LEARNS THE TRUTH...

WHAT?! YOU'RE *FLASH'S* BOY PROTÉGÉ -- *KID FLASH?!*

THAT'S RIGHT, MR. PARKER! AND I -- LIVE AROUND HERE --

AS THE TWO RAPIDLY STRIKE UP A FRIENDSHIP...

WELL, I'M SURE GLAD YOU CAME ALONG JUST NOW-- WHOEVER YOU ARE!

I CAN'T TELL HIM MY REAL IDENTITY-- I PROMISED FLASH TO KEEP IT A SECRET!

BUT, MR. PARKER--

--WHO WERE THOSE MEN YOU WERE FIGHTING WITH? WHAT WERE THEY AFTER?

BEATS ME, KID FLASH! I NEVER SAW THEM BEFORE!

BRIEFLY, THE YOUTH ADVISER RELATES WHAT LED UP TO THE UNEXPECTED ATTACK...

...AND I WAS LEAVING THE NEW SCHOOL SITE WHEN THOSE TWO LIT INTO ME! I HAVEN'T THE FAINTEST-- WAIT A MINUTE! I JUST THOUGHT OF SOMETHING!

SINCE YOU LIVE AROUND HERE, KID FLASH-- YOU PROBABLY KNOW THAT LATELY, AS CITY YOUTH ADVISER, I'VE HAD SOME TROUBLE WITH AN OUTFIT...

...SELLING THE SPEEDY GO-MOBILES-- LITTLE AUTOS THAT ARE SUPPOSED TO BE FUN FOR KIDS, BUT REALLY GO MUCH TOO FAST FOR JUST FUN!

I KNOW...

"ONLY THIS MORNING I SAW A COUPLE OF KIDS PLAYING 'CHICKEN' IN THEIR NEW GO-MOBILES!"

153

"THEY SPED AT EACH OTHER, TO SEE WHICH ONE WOULD GIVE WAY! ONLY--THEY CAME TOO CLOSE AND COLLIDED!"

THAT GO-MOBILE-- OVERTURNING! THE DRIVER WILL BE HURT--!

"NO ONE WAS WATCHING ME... THEY WERE ALL WATCHING THE COLLISION..."

"...AND IN THAT INSTANT BEFORE ANYONE COULD NOTICE, I BECAME KID FLASH!"

"AT SUPER-SPEED I MANAGED TO REACH THE DRIVER AND PULL HIM OUT OF THE OVERTURNING CAR BEFORE ANYTHING COULD HAPPEN TO HIM!"

...SO FORTUNATELY NO ONE WAS INJURED!

BUT YOU MEAN, MR. PARKER, THAT YOU SUSPECT THE GO-MOBILE SALESMEN OF ATTACKING YOU?

THEY MAY HAVE HIRED THUGS TO DO THEIR DIRTY WORK!

THEY KNOW I'VE BEEN CAMPAIGNING TO GET THE CITY TO BAR THE SALE OF THEIR VEHICLES TO CHILDREN--AS TOO DANGEROUS!

I SEE! LOOK-- THERE'S THE AGENCY NOW!

AS THE BOY SPEEDSTER ACTS ON IMPULSE...

JUST A MOMENT, MR. PARKER! I'M GOING TO DO A LITTLE INVESTIGATING HERE -- IN MY OWN WAY!

REMICK

I WONDER WHAT THAT AMAZING YOUNGSTER HOPES TO FIND OUT?

GO-MOBILE AGENCY

ED REMICK, PROP.

WHEN KID FLASH REAPPEARS...

NO--IT COULDN'T HAVE BEEN THE GO-MOBILE PEOPLE, MR. PARKER! THEY CLOSED UP THE AGENCY AND LEFT TOWN A FEW DAYS AGO--I SPOKE TO THE OWNER OF THE BUILDING!

HMM! IN THAT CASE--

--THERE'S ANOTHER POSSIBILITY, KID FLASH! THE ATTACK ON ME TOOK PLACE RIGHT AFTER I LEFT THE SITE OF THE NEW SCHOOL! I HAD GONE THERE...

...BECAUSE I FIGURED THE BIG ACE CONSTRUCTION COMPANY MIGHT HAVE SOME NEW METHODS OF CONSTRUCTION--THAT WOULD ENABLE THEM TO FINISH THE SCHOOL SO FAST! I WANTED TO LEARN ABOUT THEM ...

BUT I DIDN'T FIND ANYTHING, ALTHOUGH I LOOKED AROUND! IT WAS SCARCELY FIVE MINUTES LATER THAT THOSE THUGS POUNCED ON ME!

MAIN ST.

ONE WAY

JUMPING JETS! I WONDER--

155

SUDDENLY...

UHH--! BREAKING THROUGH! THIS **PROVES**--

AS THE SPEEDY YOUTH NIMBLY VAULTS BACK INTO THE ROOM ...

--THAT THE FLOOR THEY'VE BUILT HERE WOULD ONLY LAST A YEAR OR SO, MR. PARKER! NOW LET'S TRY THE GYMNASIUM EQUIPMENT DOWNSTAIRS!

THEN, AS **KID FLASH** PUTS THE EQUIPMENT IN THE GYM TO HIS AMAZING TIME-TEST...

THESE FLYING RINGS WOULD BREAK IN ABOUT A YEAR!

THIS TRAPEZE BAR WOULDN'T LAST SIX MONTHS!

THERE GO THE PARALLEL BARS--THEY'RE DEFECTIVE TOO!

DO YOU REALIZE WHAT THIS MEANS? THIS BUILDING IS A **FRAUD!** IT'S BUILT TO LAST ONLY A COUPLE OF YEARS--AND THAT'S WHY THE **BIG ACE COMPANY** WAS ABLE TO SUBMIT SUCH A **LOW BID!**

RIGHT, MR. PARKER! NOW LET'S GO AND...

YOU TWO AIN'T GOIN' NO-WHERE--

THE TWO THUGS--

--WHO ATTACKED YOU BEFORE!

THIS TIME WE'LL TAKE CARE OF THAT SNOOPER-- AND DO IT **RIGHT!**

AN' THAT INCLUDES THE KID IN COSTUME!

KID FLASH-- LOOK OUT! THEY'VE GOT GUNS...

GOT TO REACH THEM BEFORE THEY CAN FIRE--!

THE **BOY SPEEDSTER** UTILIZES THE INTERVENING HURDLE TO GAIN MOMENTUM IN HIS PLUNGE FORWARD, AND...

GREAT SCOTT! HE BOWLED THEM OVER BEFORE THEY COULD EVEN PULL A TRIGGER!

GRAB THIS GUN, MR. PARKER-- KEEP IT ON THESE MUGS!

AFTER THE ATTACKERS HAVE BEEN HERDED TO POLICE HEADQUARTERS...

SO IT LOOKS LIKE YOU --AND **KID FLASH--** HAVE UNCOVERED AN **ATTEMPTED SWINDLE,** MR. PARKER! OUR INVESTIGATION SHOWS THE **BIG ACE COMPANY** HAS PULLED THIS IN OTHER TOWNS--THEY PUT UP A "QUICKIE" SCHOOL BUILDING FOR A CHEAP PRICE--

--BUT THE BUILDING BARELY LASTS LONG ENOUGH FOR THEM TO GET OUT OF TOWN WITH THEIR ILL--GOTTEN PROFITS!

WE'LL NEED A *NEW BUILDING* ALTOGETHER, MR. PARKER...

...AND AS CHAIRMAN OF THE SCHOOL BOARD I'M GOING TO RECOMMEND THAT *YOU* ERECT IT! BUT CAN YOU FINISH THE JOB BY *SEPTEMBER*?

I--I CAN TRY!

AT THE END OF THE WEEK...

RALPH, YOU WOULDN'T HAVE A *CHANCE* TO FINISH THE SCHOOL IN TIME--EXCEPT FOR ONE THING! THE ENTIRE STUDENT BODY HAS AGREED TO GIVE YOU A HELPING HAND!

I UNDERSTAND IT WAS *KID FLASH* WHO TALKED THE STUDENTS INTO GIVING UP THEIR SUMMER VACATION FOR THIS PROJECT!

YES, WE HAVE A LOT TO THANK THAT AMAZING YOUNGSTER FOR, LINDA...

NO DOUBT ABOUT THAT, RALPH-- THE WHOLE TOWN DOES!

The End 3/2

*T*HERE'LL BE MORE *KID FLASH* STORIES IN FUTURE ISSUES--IF YOU READERS ASK FOR THEM! Write to *The Flash*